IGY:
YEAR
OF
DISCOVERY

ANN ARBOR   **the university of michigan press**

I G Y :

YEAR

OF

DISCOVERY

the story of the
International Geophysical Year, 1957-58

by SYDNEY CHAPMAN

Designed by Stuart Ross

Copyright © by The University of Michigan 1959

Fourth printing November 1960

Published in the United States of America by
The University of Michigan Press and simultaneously
in Toronto, Canada, by Ambassador Books Ltd.
Library of Congress Catalog Card No. 59-9733
Manufactured in the United States of America
Copyright is not claimed for illustrations bearing credit lines.

*The first book rights in this book have been given
by the author to the Comité Spécial de l'Année
Géophysique Internationale, for IGY purposes, and to the
Regents of The University of Michigan for the benefit of the
Department of Aeronautical and Astronautical Engineering.*

DEDICATION

to: **PAULETTE DOYEN, PHILLIP MANGE, MICHAEL BAKER, MAURICE HAUTFENNE, FRANCINE HAUTFENNE,**

who at the IGY Secretariat in Brussels and at the meetings of the IGY committee at Brussels, Rome, Barcelona, and Moscow have given splendid service to the International Geophysical Year.

The time will come when the International Geophysical Year will be viewed as an important but primitive contribution to the exploration of the cosmos.

The above words are taken from the author's closing presidential address at the last IGY congress, Moscow, August 1958.

FOREWORD

By James A. Van Allen

This book is an exception to the common observation
that the history of scientific achievement is seldom written
by the major participants themselves.
Professor Sydney Chapman's narrative account
of the International Geophysical Year is notable for the insight,
the breadth of scope, and the enthusiasm which can be conveyed
only by the leader of a great enterprise.
Lively and readable, it will engage the attention
of every person who has an interest in the natural phenomena
of the world in which he lives.
Its authority will make it a valuable reference
for active research workers in geophysics
and an enthralling guide for students.
Only to the discerning eyes of professional colleagues
will it be evident that Professor Chapman's immense personal
contributions to the science of geophysics provided many of
the intellectual "steel wires" which unified the diverse and
multifold undertakings of the International Geophysical Year.
Throughout the long period of preparation for
and execution of the I.G.Y., Professor Chapman
discharged the arduous duties of President of
the Bureau du Comité Spécial de l'Année Géophysique Internationale 1957–58
with wisdom, with grace, and with dispatch.
Yet he continued his teaching and personal research
and never lacked time for consultation
with aspiring students and young colleagues.

PREFACE

This book offers a popular account of some scientific aspects of the earth and sun—in special connection with the 1957–58 enterprise called the International Geophysical Year (IGY).

The text, based on four lectures given in October 1958 at The University of Michigan, is addressed in the first place to an American audience. The illustrations, mainly gathered by The University of Michigan Press, are largely taken from American sources, because of ready availability.

I am not expert in all the fields with which this book deals. Hence I have consulted some of the IGY Reporters—as indicated on p. 102—and others, about the text and diagrams.

As well as to the Reporters, I am indebted for advice and information or illustrations to the following: Professor K. E. Bullen, Dr. G. E. R. Deacon, Mr. R. T. Hansen, Dr. William Markowitz, Dr. Helen Dodson Prince, the Royal Society of London, and to other persons, agencies, and sources named in the picture credits.

Finally, I wish to acknowledge many helpful courtesies rendered during the preparation of this book by Dr. Wilbur C. Nelson, Chairman, and other members of the Department of Aeronautical and Astronautical Engineering of The University of Michigan, and by the officials of The University of Michigan Press.

S.C.

CONTENTS

When the moon eclipses the sun, an outer solar atmosphere called the corona becomes visible. This photograph of it was taken at Green River, Wyoming, by astronomers of the Mount Wilson Observatory, California, on June 8, 1918, a year after sunspot maximum. The sun rotates about an axis whose northern and southern poles are indicated. Several bright prominences are visible at the edge of the sun. The shape of the corona, which changes during the sunspot cycle, was somewhat triangular, with the apex on the left (the eastern side). The corona was brilliant and bluish white (see page 88).

THE EARTH AND OCEANS

Among the ancient Greeks some philosophers taught that all things are compounded from four elements—earth, water, air and fire. In the great study of our planet and the sun that is known as the International Geophysical Year (IGY), all four of these so-called elements were involved. Much of the massive earth lies under a relatively very shallow covering of water—the oceans. Above lies the mantle of air, the atmosphere. This is greatly influenced from afar by the fiery sun.

The major aim of the IGY was to improve our knowledge and understanding of the earth and its more rapid changes. To do this it was essential also to improve our knowledge and understanding of the sun and its changes. Thus the IGY was a study of the earth and the sun.

It was an immense undertaking, remarkable in many ways. Time will be needed to reap its harvest, which will benefit mankind.

But still it is well to remember that the IGY started from a great fund of knowledge built up by our forerunners. The IGY speeded up the advance of this knowledge. And by its careful planning and simultaneous observations in related fields it will give much more understanding than would the same effort applied in a haphazard way.

On the earth the most continual and rapid changes occur in the atmosphere. There are weather changes at the lower levels, and higher up there are what one may call electrical weather changes. These occur in the ionosphere, the region where radio waves are usefully deflected round the bend of the earth: their transmission can be much affected by the electrical weather in that region. The electrical weather shows itself also in disturbances of the earth's magnetism, all over the globe. In the higher latitudes it shows as auroras, the beautiful polar lights.

The IGY had two ancestors, the two International Polar Years—the first one seventy-five years before, in 1882–83, the second one twenty-five years before, in 1932–33. The aim of the first Polar Year was to study the atmospheric changes—ordinary weather, and electrical weather as shown by magnetic storms and the polar lights. This was also the aim of the second Polar Year; but by then radio had been developed and was used as an additional means of studying the electrical weather in the ionosphere.

The original main aim of the IGY was to advance our knowledge of these atmospheric changes, with improved instruments, in greater detail, and over an extended area of the globe, including the Antarctic. It was known that the electrical weather, at least, was greatly influenced by changes on the sun. Hence solar observations also were to be improved and intensified.

But the lower atmosphere and its weather —so important to mankind—affect the oceans and are affected by them. Hence oceanography, the scientific investigation of the oceans, was made an important part of the program. For similar reasons the study of the glaciers was included. They change much more slowly than the atmosphere, and more slowly also than the oceans. But still they lock up much water in solid form, and they do grow and decay. It is not so necessary to study them all at the same time as in the case of the atmosphere and oceans. But many of them are in high arctic and antarctic latitudes, where ordinarily there are few people or none to study them. The IGY, when many scientific groups were to be observing in those regions, offered exceptional and economical opportunities of also studying the glaciers. Hence

it was decided to take stock of the world's glaciers during the program. The record obtained will give a reliable basis to determine how they have changed, when another IGY is held at some future time.

The solid earth also changes, as geologists tell us. But the changes they consider are far slower than those even of the glaciers. Only its magnetism changes with comparable rapidity; this aspect of the earth was already partly included in the program. Otherwise, it might seem as though there was no reason to step up or co-ordinate the study of the solid earth during the IGY.

However, this was done—and for two good reasons. One was the same as has been mentioned in connection with the glaciers—there would be groups of scientists in regions where the earth had been little studied. A slight addition to costs and manpower for such expeditions would enable gaps to be filled in our knowledge of the solid earth.

The other reason was that some studies of the solid earth, particularly of its large-scale topography, depend partly on radio time signals between distant astronomical observatories. The intensive studies of the electrical weather of the upper atmosphere would enable the time of passage of such signals to be estimated with exceptional accuracy.

Hence the program was extended to include several aspects of the solid earth—its form and size and rotation, its gravitational attraction, its bodily tides, and its earthquakes. The earthquakes give our best means of studying the earth's interior.

The whole program was divided into fourteen parts. For each part one member of the central international committee is responsible. He is called the Reporter for that sub-

The great stresses in unstable regions of the earth's crust are partially relieved from time to time by earthquakes. Sometimes they generate volcanic eruptions. A notable example is the Bárcena Volcano here shown. It is on the small Mexican island San Benedicto (19.3° N, 110.8° W, south of the Gulf of California). The volcano was born on August 1, 1952. In 12 days a cone of pumice grew up, to a height of 1200 feet above sea level, while immense masses of fiery clouds enveloped the volcano. Later the crater became plugged up, and lava poured out from cracks in the side of the mountain, forming a delta. All activity had ceased, and strong erosion had begun, by the end of 1953.

ject (p. 102). Five Reporters deal with the IGY programs for the earth and oceans.

The program in these subjects aimed to extend the already wide bounds of our existing knowledge—by old and new instruments and methods, particularly in areas previously little studied. To understand what the IGY attempted in these fields, it is necessary to consider briefly the stage they had reached before it began.

The geographical exploration of the surface of the globe has progressed through the centuries. It is now almost complete. The Antarctic is the only major region still largely unexplored. The IGY will do much to fill the gap, but mainly incidentally, as part of its physical researches. The IGY did not aim to explore the Antarctic continent so fully as would enable the whole region to be well mapped. However, new geographical features of the Antarctic were found during the IGY—new mountain ranges, ice-free areas, and information about level of land under ice-cover.

The earth is nearly spherical; the irregularities of its land surface range at most from about six miles above to about seven miles below sea level. The average heights above and depths below sea level are much less than six miles. But the earth does not have a completely spherical shape. Sea level at the north and south poles is about thirteen miles nearer to the earth's center than it is at the equator. This flattening is related to the earth's rotation. Moreover, even the sea level surface is not quite regularly ellipsoidal—it is misshapen in a more general way, apart from minor irregularities depending on winds and currents, such as are shown by a smoothly eddying river.

The task of the men who make flat maps that represent a large area of the earth—such as North America or Europe—is difficult. It would be so even were the earth truly spherical. Its polar flattening, and still more its major irregularities, complicate the task. The standard of achievement in making flat maps depends on the exactness of our knowledge of the actual form and size of the earth.

If it were truly spherical its radius could be found by measuring the distance between two points on it, and also finding by means of star observations the angle between the plumb lines at the two places. Owing to the earth's rotation the plumb lines would not hang quite exactly towards the earth's center, but the small deflections on this account can be allowed for.

Actually the earth is irregular not only in form, but also the distribution of mass within

it is not quite regular. Hence the plumb line direction, corrected for the rotation, is generally not quite radial. It may be deflected, for example, by a mountain range—generally the deflection, surprisingly, is not toward the range, but away from it. This is because the mountain ranges have deep roots going down into denser matter, in which they partly float. Moreover, the strength of the earth's attraction, as well as its direction, varies from place to place. At sea level it is greater at the poles than at the equator, because the poles are nearer the center of the earth.

Hence, in order to know the true form and size of the earth, it is desirable to measure the strength of the attraction as fully as possible all over the surface. The instruments used are called gravimeters: they may be refined spring balances, nowadays generally made

Many noncommercial ships visited the Arctic and Antarctic during the International Geophysical Year. Some were floating laboratories from which scientists made observations of many kinds—of weather, sea temperature, currents, chemical composition, radioactivity, or the nature of the sea bed. Others carried the scientists and their equipment and supplies to the Antarctic continent or to islands—including the floating ice islands in the Arctic. This picture shows two U. S. Coast Guard vessels, "Bramble" on the left, "Storia" on the right, photographed from a third, "Spar." They were engaged on a mission through the Arctic seas and were the first American vessels to complete the northwest passage from the Atlantic to the Pacific Ocean—a difficult voyage attempted unsuccessfully many times during the nineteenth century. One of the worst parts of the passage is here shown—the ships are crunching their way through Simpson Strait.

of quartz, or accurate and rather complicated pendulums. They have been greatly improved in recent years, and on land a gravity survey is now made much more speedily and accurately than formerly. As the oceans cover the major part of the earth, the gravity there also must be measured. The lack of a fixed platform on which to place the instrument is naturally a great difficulty.

A Dutch scientist, Vening Meinesz, was confronted with the same problem, in a minor degree, in making a gravity survey of Holland, where the spongy soil was sometimes not firm enough to support his instruments with enough steadiness. About forty years ago he invented a triple-pendulum gravimeter that overcame the difficulty. Thirty years ago (1927) he went on to use the same instrument in a submarine, which when submerged is steadier than a surface ship. In this way he made some excellent ocean gravity measurements in a voyage of a Dutch submarine from Europe to the East Indies. The submarine went under water when measurements were to be taken. The results were especially interesting in the region of the great ocean trench off the East Indies. It was he who made most of the 1200 good ocean gravity measurements recorded by the end of World War II.

The same method has since been applied elsewhere also during the IGY. But it is not easy to obtain the use of submarines for such a purpose. Hence it is promising for the future that the IGY has seen the first successful trial on the open ocean of a new instrument and method applicable on a surface ship. The instrument, invented by Anton Graf of

Munich, Germany, is used on a gyro-stabilized platform on the vessel. The platform has to be carefully leveled. On the right is a half-hour record thus made on the U.S.S. "Compass Island" during the trial voyage from and back to New York, November 18–22, 1957. The disturbances due to the vibrations of the ship were reduced by a factor of several thousand. The results were tested against those made ten years earlier aboard a U.S. submarine. The agreement is so good as to encourage the hope that the new equipment will come to be used on many oceanographic survey vessels as the standard method.

World maps showing accurately the strength of gravity all over the globe have many gaps, some on land but more over the ocean. The IGY will partly fill in the gap over the Antarctic continent and over the oceans, but much will still remain for future surveys.

The present gravity maps form one basis for our knowledge of the size and form of the earth, and of the distribution of its mass. The irregularities of distribution of the force of gravity extend, to a decreasing extent, into the space round the earth. They will affect the motions of the man-made satellites, and the study of the satellite orbits may thus throw additional light on the form and on the interior of the earth.

Along with the gravity measurements go measurements of distances over the earth's surface. The highest grade surveys by levels and theodolites are called "geodetic." They relate to a substantial area of the earth, over which the curvature of the surface cannot be ignored. Instead, it must be carefully measured. Differences of latitude and of longitude

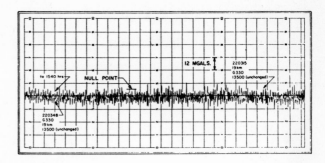

This half-hour record of the Graf gravimeter, though jaggedly disturbed by sea waves of about an eight-second period, permits accurate measurement of changes in the earth's attraction along the course of the vessel. The change was two parts in 10,000 in a 12-hour voyage.

This beautiful picture of the full moon was taken at the U. S. Naval Observatory, Washington, D.C. It shows the great areas called "seas" by early astronomers, though they are probably plains covered with dust whose depth may be a hazard for future explorers of our companion planet. These moon visitors will also study the many craters, large and small, that are a feature so much more prominent on the moon than on the earth. The origin of the craters—whether volcanic, or due to the impact of great meteors—may then become clear.

are measured at astronomical observatories to a high order of accuracy. Time astronomically measured at observatories in different longitudes must be compared. Formerly this was done by carrying good chronometers from one to the other; now radio time signals are used. They travel with the speed of light, but their time of travel must be allowed for. This is not easy to determine with the desired accuracy, because they travel along a curved path, and their speed is affected by the electrical properties of the atmosphere. Hence the observations of the radio scientists have to be brought into the calculations.

New types of clocks have been devised in recent decades. They have gradually attained an accuracy and reliability that exceed those of the rotating earth itself, which in the past has been the ultimate standard of time measurement. Formerly the clocks of astronomical observatories had to be constantly checked by star observations. During a long cloudy period the uncertainty in the precise time increased because of the imperfections of the clocks. Now quartz crystal clocks are able to check the regularity of the earth itself. That is to say, they can detect slight irregularities in its rate of rotation. These must be caused by shifts of matter on or within the earth. In addition, the clocks together with the star observations can detect minute wobbles of the earth's axis, partly caused by the attraction of the sun and moon on the earth. The wobbles depend on the varying positions of the sun and moon, and on the departure of the earth itself from spherical symmetry. One of the new instruments to be used in the program is the Danjon astrolabe, designed by the IGY Reporter for longitudes and latitudes. It makes use of a basin of mercury and a 60° prism to form two images of a star, direct and reflected. The instant of coincidence of the two images, when the altitude of the star is 60°, is measured by the observer in a way not affected by personal error. Astronomical longitude and latitude are found by so measuring a number of stars in different azimuths. The astronomical co-ordinates of an observatory can be determined within about 5 feet. Any slow change of position of the observatory that may occur by earth movements—such as the suggested drift of the continents over the earth's crust—could in time be detected by such observations repeated at different epochs. But the distances between observations in different continents are not so well determined. Their estimation depends on the gravity survey as well as on trigonometrical surveying.

The earth's form and size and rotation were studied during the program also in a quite different way. The method is geometrical and does not involve gravity measurements. It depends on observations of the moon by cameras attached to telescopes. Such photography was undertaken at twenty observatories distributed over the earth. They employed a special type of camera invented by Dr. W. Markowitz of the U. S. Naval Observatory.

Two difficulties beset such photography. The moon is so bright that its image is fogged on the plate, if the exposure is long enough to show the background stars. These are necessary to give the moon's position. This difficulty is overcome by placing a shaded glass disc that covers the image of the moon on the plate. This reduces the brightness of the image and eliminates fogging. The second difficulty is that the moon is moving across the stellar background. The telescope can be made to follow the star motion, so that the star images are sharp. But the moon's relative motion will blur its image. Dr. Markowitz overcame this difficulty by a mechanism that tilts the obscuring glass disc at just the right rate to keep the moon image constant on the photographic plate. This in effect gives an instantaneous determination of the moon's position upon the stellar background. Seen from different observatories at the same instant, the moon occupies different positions relative to the stars. Each observatory makes two or more such observations during the night. Calculations from such observations will determine the geometry of the observatory distribution over the earth, independent of gravity. Intercontinental distances will be

measured with errors of the order of no more than 100 to 200 feet. At present the uncertainty is greater. The positions of some ocean islands are uncertain by a mile.

This program will also give an improved orbit of the moon, and a more accurate standard of time measurement. This is needed to calibrate recently developed atomic frequency clocks of high precision, such as those of cesium. The moon time depends on the gravitational control of the moon by earth and sun, the atomic time does not; a long continued comparison between them will be of great future interest. The results of this work are expected about 1960.

The Markowitz dual-rate camera and telescope used during the IGY to determine the moon's position with great accuracy. This composite photograph shows also how the moon appears, reduced in brightness by the dark filter that is placed over the center of the photographic plate. The tilting mechanism for the filter is at the side of the camera.

The Bondasca Glacier in the Bregaglia Valley in the Swiss Alps. Great mountain systems like the Alps, Himalayas, Rockies, and Andes have deep "roots," sometimes extending down into the denser semiplastic layers beneath, sometimes resting on the down-curved rather rigid crust. Thus, in a sense they float on the denser material below.

THE SOLID
AND LIQUID EARTH

Astronomers determine the earth's form and size, its rotation and the slight wobbles of its axis, and its motion with the moon round the sun. In addition to the wobbles caused by the attraction of the moon and sun, acting on the nonspherical earth, the earth has small wobbles of its own. These, like its rotation, are slightly inconstant, owing to movements of water and air from place to place over the surface and to movements within the earth. All these wobbles depend also on the large-scale elasticity of the earth—on the extent to which it yields to changing forces of gravity or rotation. By and large it behaves as if its elasticity were similar to that of steel.

Information about the large-scale elasticity of the earth can also be got by measuring its bodily tides. The tidal forces exerted by the moon and, to a less extent, by the sun, act not only on the oceans but also on the atmosphere and the solid earth. The oceans and atmosphere can flow under the influence of these tidal forces. The solid earth only becomes elastically distorted. The earth tides are measured by exceptionally delicate gravimeters—sensitive to a billionth of the force of gravity at the earth's surface. This change of gravity would correspond to that experienced in a change of distance from the earth's center by an eighteenth of an inch. Earth tide records were taken during the International Geophysical Year at a number of places over the earth. The tidal "breathing" thus measured amounts to only a few inches up and down, twice daily. Its measurement helps us understand the nature of the earth.

Earthquake Waves

By far the richest source of knowledge about the inside of the earth is the study of its rapid quivering movements. These are related to earthquakes of all degrees of intensity. The earthquakes set up several kinds of waves, which travel along the surface and throughout almost the whole earth. Thus they provide information about its nature almost down to the very center.

At many places spread over the globe there are recorders of earthquake waves—called seismometers. Similarly, the science of earthquakes is called seismology, and those who study it are seismologists. Usually an earthquake recording station has at least three instruments that register the movements in three perpendicular directions.

During the IGY the number of earthquake recording stations was increased by more than 100 to a total of about 330. Some countries then set up their first such stations; others increased the number of their stations. Many of the new stations, however, were in regions where earthquakes had scarcely ever been recorded—12 in the Arctic, 18 in the Antarctic, and 72 in low latitudes. Besides increasing the number of recording stations, the IGY had a good effect on some existing stations. It speeded up the measurement of their records, and their dispatch to the international office where such material is collected (p. 97).

Besides the standard instruments, new types were devised and installed—some to measure waves within special frequency

The thickness of the Antarctic ice was explored in many places, as here, by artificial earthquake waves caused by explosions. The waves traveled downward through the ice and an echo was returned from the bedrock. Its time delay, recorded by equipment carried on the Sno-Cat, gave the depth of the ice. The U. S. party made many such measurements during an oversnow traverse from the Byrd IGY Station.

ranges, or waves of low intensity. These are called microseisms. Other instruments measured slow changes of strain in the rocks. Such instruments are called extensometers or strain seismometers. Their purpose is similar to that of the devices used to measure slow changes—settlements and cracks—in old buildings, such as St. Paul's Cathedral, London. Two piers about 25 yards apart are firmly sunk and concreted into the rock in a tunnel. A quartz bar firmly attached to one of them extends to the other, where it helps to record the slow changes of distance between them. Two stations for such records have been set up in South America. One is high in the Andes, the other is on the nearby low-lying coastal plain. At each station there are two such tunnels at right angles.

In some regions of the earth slow changes are occurring underground—in the upper crust or at deeper levels. They gradually build up stresses and strains, which from time to time are relieved by a sudden shift or dislocation. From this point—called the focus— earthquake waves travel out in all directions. The intensity of the quake felt at any particular place depends on its distance from the focus, on the depth of the focus, and on the nature of the dislocation. The greater earth-

quakes can be recorded all over the earth.

Earthquake sources are not distributed at random over the globe—there are certain belts where earthquakes occur with special frequency and intensity. These have been mapped. They are found to be associated with large structural features of the earth, especially along the borders of the great oceans, and along chains of islands, many of which may be volcanic.

The elastic waves set up by a sudden shift of mass at the focus of an earthquake are of four main kinds. In two of them the waves travel in the body of the earth, and in the other two the waves keep near the earth's surface. Of the "body" waves, one kind resembles the sound waves in air; these are called P waves. They involve compression and rarefaction, by alternating motion of the quivering matter, back and forth along the direction of wave travel. Such P waves may be thought of as "push-and-pull" waves. "Body" waves of the other kind are called S waves or "shake" waves. The movements in them are at right angles to the direction of wave travel. They depend on the rigidity of the matter through which they progress, in other words, on its power to resist deformation. In fluids, like air or water, this power is

Earth strains, caused by stresses that may build up to breaking strength and culminate in a disastrous earthquake, are here being measured in a tunnel in granite bedrock near Azusa, California. The apparatus was designed by Dr. Hugo Benioff (shown in the foreground), professor at the California Institute of Technology. Besides measuring the strain in the surrounding rock, the ultrasensitive gage reacts to the shaking motion of the rock set up by great earthquakes even from the most distant parts of the world. It is hoped to work out a system of prediction of earthquakes that may save many lives, by a network of such gages, and by a continuing study of how great earthquakes develop.

weak, so that S waves cannot travel in them. But fluids resist changes of volume, and so they can transmit P waves.

Waves of these different kinds travel in the same material at different speeds. Hence, starting from the same focus, they reach distant places at different times. The P waves come first, later the S waves and other types. Thus the earthquake record, even of the simplest quake with only one sudden underground dislocation, is drawn out over many seconds. The interval between the first arrivals of the P and S waves gives some indication of the distance from the focus.

Waves of each kind also vary in speed, according to the nature of the material through which they travel. If this changes gradually along their course, their path is curved. If they come to a surface separating different kinds of material, they are partly reflected back into the region within which they approach the surface. They also travel into the other region, in a new direction—there they are said to be refracted or bent at the interface. At such a surface, also, either P or S waves can set up both P and S waves.

The material of which the earth is made does vary with depth, and there are interfaces separating different kinds of earth-substance. Consequently, the waves from even the simplest earthquake are curved, and they multiply in number as they reach the interfaces. Only after long study and experience have seismologists learned how to decipher the records of earthquake waves—to recognize the traces of different kinds, and to infer their paths—and whether they have come all the way from the focus or been generated by reflection or refraction of such original waves.

As a result, a large amount of astonishingly detailed and definite information has been gained about the inside of the earth. This is found to consist of a number of layers. Each seems to be fairly uniform in thickness, except for the layers nearest the surface. The outermost crust, down to a depth of 20 to 30 miles, is irregular in its constitution and in its upper and lower surfaces. The oceans cover the lower parts of its outer surface; continents and islands extend above the sea level, and mountains and mountain chains rise up both on land and from the sea bed.

Only the outermost layer of this crust is open to direct study by geologists, either at the surface, or in quarries or mines.

Despite the wealth of knowledge gained by the geologists, some fundamental problems of the outer crust remain unsolved—for example, how mountain ranges and the deep ocean trenches are formed, and how granite and sediments have come to be intermingled as they are.

Below the outer crust there is a thick layer called the mantle. This is divided by seismologists into four layers (B, C, D′, D″) with

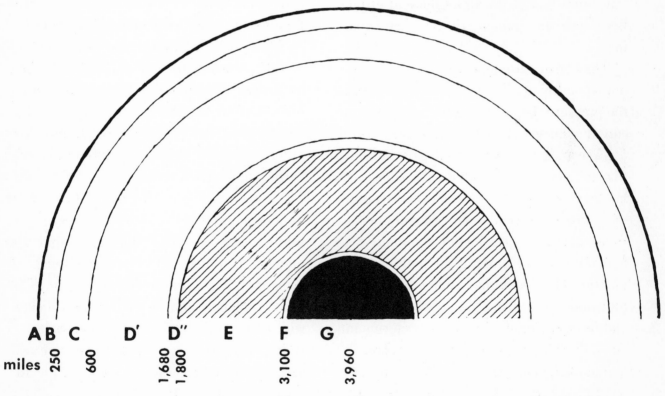

Schematic cross section showing, roughly to scale, the several layers whose presence within the earth is inferred from the worldwide study of earthquake waves. Layer A is the outer crust of the solid earth. Its thickness is irregular, greater where mountains rise high, and less below the oceans. The next four layers, B, C, D′, D″, comprise what is called the *mantle* of the earth. This transmits both push-and-pull waves and transverse ("shake") waves. The speeds of transmission differ from layer to layer. Below the mantle is the *core*. Its upper part is a liquid layer E, that does not transmit shake waves. This surrounds an innermost solid core G, with a thin transition layer F between. The depths of the surfaces of the layers, and to the earth's center, are shown in miles.

recognizably different properties. The depth of the lower surface of the mantle is very close to 1800 miles. Below that is the core of the earth. This also is considered to include different parts, three in number, E, F, G. They are called the outer core, the transition layer and the inner core. The conclusions as to these seven layers below the crust are based on their different elastic properties, inferred from the study of the waves from many earthquakes recorded all over the globe.

The pressure steadily increases downwards, because of the weight of the overlying material. At the center the pressure reaches a colossal value—over three and one-half million times that of the atmosphere at ground level (which is about 15 lbs. per square inch).

The density also increases downward, but not smoothly at all depths, as in the case of the pressure. Especially at the surface of the core it suddenly changes; and there also the S waves cease to penetrate. This indicates that the outer core is liquid. The inner core, however, seems to be solid. The density gradually increases from about two and one-half times that of water, in the outer crust, to five and one-half times at the bottom of the mantle. There it jumps suddenly to about nine and one-half just inside the outer core, and increases gradually to about eleven and one-half at the bottom of the outer core.

The attraction of gravity varies by only about 1 per cent through the whole distance from the crust surface to the top of the core. Then it gradually decreases to zero at the center of the core.

The internal temperature is less certainly known. In deep mines it increases downward at the rate of about 50°F. per mile. If this rate continued to the center, the temperature there would exceed 180,000°F. The central temperature, in fact, is thought to be only a few thousand degrees. The high rate of increasing temperature in the crust is probably caused there by the heat of radioactive substances, such as uranium.

Thus the conditions deep in the earth are determined more by the enormous pressures than by the more moderate temperatures.

Whereas the outer crust is composed largely of sediments and igneous rocks such as granite, the mantle is thought to consist mainly of an ultrabasic rock called olivine (magnesium-iron orthosilicate). It may take different crystalline forms in different layers, corresponding to different ranges of pressure. The outer core is generally thought to consist largely of iron or nickel-iron. But other possibilities have also been suggested—that the material is yet another form of olivine, or even that it is compressed hydrogen. The inner core may consist of iron and nickel, with perhaps also some denser materials.

It will be a year or two before the increased earthquake records obtained during the In-

A twelve-hour record from Dr. Benioff's instrument (p. 24) to measure earth strains. This record comes from Isabella, California, and was made on December 4, 1957. The smooth part of the curve shows the tidal movement in the rocks, equivalent to about a third of an inch change in 2000 miles. The big movements near the middle show the waves from the considerable earthquake that occurred that day in Mongolia, over 6000 miles away. The letters mark the arrival of waves traveling by different paths through the earth.

ternational Geophysical Year are thoroughly studied. But some interesting discoveries have already been made. The Russians report that their Antarctic records indicate that the continent itself is not prone to earthquakes, except minor ones, some of which may be due to sudden cracking of great sheets of ice. But the continent is surrounded by an earthquake belt that is probably connected with the belts round the Pacific, Indian and Atlantic oceans (p. 97).

Some branches of earth science must rely solely on observation of what happens naturally. But seismology, the study of the earth's elasticity, is partly an experimental science. Without depending only on natural earthquakes, much can be learned by artificial disturbances caused by explosions. This method has the advantage that the waves start from a known place at a known time; and they are observed along a line of suitably spaced recorders, set up for the experiment. This method is much used in prospecting for useful minerals, as well as for purely scientific studies. It is applied not only on land but also at sea—for the study of the earth's crust. In this way it is found that the crust is generally thinner under the deep oceans than on land. The method is applied also over the Antarctic, Greenland, and other ice caps, to determine the ice thickness and the form of the underlying land. Such artificial earthquakes are generally mild—they are made with moderate amounts of ordinary explosive.

Accidental large explosions, such as one that occurred at Oppau, Germany, in 1921 have also been "turned to seismological advantage." In 1947 (April 18) 4000 tons of TNT left over from World War II was exploded on Heligoland, partly for scientific study. The results proved interesting, and set off lively debates among seismologists. Before and since then there have been more powerful explosions, in tests of atomic bombs and H bombs. The earthquake recorders duly registered them, and the results were valuable, but less so than they might have been because complete and precise information about the place and time of the explosions was lacking except in one case.

In 1955 an influential group of seismologists proposed that during the IGY one or more atom bombs be exploded for seismological purposes—one each in the U.S.A. and U.S.S.R., one near Australia and one in the Pacific. The proposal was not accepted, but the wish for such experiments persists. Perhaps it may be carried out in the future, under suitable conditions guarding the public safety. Meanwhile, it has led to some governmental co-operation with seismologists in the exploding of bombs for other purposes. This has already led to new knowledge of great interest concerning the earth's crust in the Australian region.

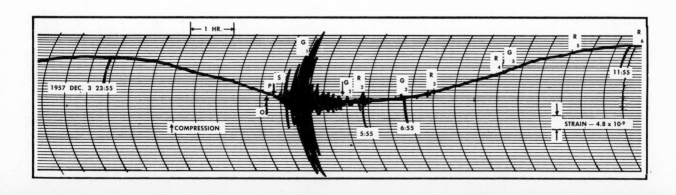

The Glaciers

The earth, that seems to us so solid, appears to have a deep liquid layer surrounding the inner core. The thick mantle above this liquid layer acts like a solid, in that it transmits shake waves. But still it may have a certain degree of fluidity, permitting very slow flow. This may be the cause of the formation of deep ocean trenches, and of the pushing together of considerable areas of the crust, to form mountain chains and massifs like the Alps, the Andes, and the Himalayas.

There is also another solid part of the earth that has some fluidity—namely, the glaciers. They also were actively studied during the IGY. They consist of snow gradually compacted into ice by the pressure of later overlying snowfall. Under great pressure ice becomes slightly fluid, somewhat like pitch, which resists quick change of form under sudden forces, but will gradually subside if left to itself. Thus the glaciers slowly flow down to lower levels from the high regions where mostly they are formed.

The volume of solid water in the glaciers is small compared with the ocean liquid volume. The total water content of the globe is of the order of 350 million cubic miles; the glaciers account for about 1 per cent of it. This estimate is rougher than it will be later, because at present the average thickness of the great Antarctic ice cap is uncertain.

In surface area the glaciers seem more important—they occupy about 10 per cent of the land area of the globe—nearly six million square miles. In some past ages there may have been no glaciers at all, in others they have been still more widespread, covering up to a third of the land area. The Antarctic ice cap, extending over nearly five million square miles, accounts for most of the present area. Next comes the Greenland ice cap, with nearly 700,000 square miles. All the others represent only about 4 per cent of the whole glacial area. They include over 130,000 square miles in the Arctic and in North America; 50,000 square miles in Asia;

The sparse glaciers of Africa were studied by two British Commonwealth IGY expeditions. One, provided by Kenya Colony, examined its Mount Kenya, just south of the equator. One of the highest mountains in Africa (17,040 ft.), it has fifteen glaciers. The two greatest are each about a mile long. A large crevasse in one of these, Lewis Glacier, is shown on the right. Most of the glaciers end a little below 15,000 ft. Old moraines show that they were once much more extensive, descending to 12,000 ft. On the left a mule team of the King's African Rifles, carrying supplies, approaches Camp Three.

The leader of the Mount Kenya IGY glaciological expedition, Dr. Igor S. Loupekine, collects rock samples in the Teleki Valley on the mountain. He is senior lecturer in geology at the Royal Technical College at the capital city, Nairobi. His team comprised eighteen men. Mount Kenya is an old volcano, now much denuded, forming several steep pyramids. The tree line ends at about 10,500 ft., then pastures (amid crags) go up to 15,000 ft. (see also pp. 46–47).

10,000 in South America; 4,000 in Europe; 400 on Pacific Islands; and in Africa only 12 square miles. One of those in Africa is the dying glacial area on Kilimanjaro in Tanganyika Territory. It was studied by a British IGY expedition early in 1958.

If all the glaciers were to melt, owing to a worldwide warmer climate, the sea level over the globe would rise by an amount that is variously estimated from 60 to 200 feet. Even the lower amount would mean the submergence of many of the world's great cities. During the last ice age the average air temperature over land at sea level was perhaps about 10° colder than now, and the sea level 250 feet lower. This would considerably increase the land area, joining regions now separated by sea, like Britain and Europe. In addition to the great Antarctic and Greenland ice sheets, there were then three others, over Europe, Siberia and North America.

The glaciers over the high broad ridge of Greenland flow slowly downward toward the coast. Where a glacier is confined between mountains, it forms a river of pressurized ice. The rate of flow varies greatly from one glacier to another. It may be only a few inches a day, or as much as 50 feet a day. The lower end may melt on land, feeding a river torrent flowing into a lake or the sea. Or the glacier may reach sea level, and push out to sea. It may rest there on a shallow sea bed or float on deeper water. Pieces may break off to become icebergs, or even ice islands—like those that were occupied before and during the IGY by American and Russian scientists.

A glacier may remain constant if the annual loss by melting is made good by new snowfall. If the two are unequal, it will become bigger or smaller. On the whole, there

The picture opposite shows an Antarctic scene— viewed from within a snow cave in the region near the U. S. IGY station at Kainan Bay (see map on page 32). The inside of the cave is being photographed by a member of the party that spent the (southern) winter of 1957 at this station. Such caves are formed by the wind and the movement of the ice. Their study provides information about the structure of the ice and about the deformation of the layers formed by successive snowfalls.

The other British IGY glaciological expedition in Africa was organized by Sheffield University, England. It studied Mt. Kilimanjaro (19,320 ft.), Tanganyika Territory, Africa's highest mountain. The picture below shows a camp at 14,500 ft., with Penck Glacier above, and, on the extreme right, remnants of Little Penck and Uhlig glaciers. Kilimanjaro has two main peaks. One is a fairly recent extinct crater. Glaciers flow through breaks in its walls and down its outer slopes.

are more and bigger glaciers where the climate is coldest, but there are exceptions to this general rule. For example, the largest glacial area in Alaska is in the relatively warm region along its southern coast, because the snowfall is the heaviest there. Even in Northern Greenland there are some areas free from glacial ice. The same is true, as the IGY expeditions have shown, in the Antarctic.

As the weather conditions vary from decade to decade or from century to century, the glaciers may grow in some regions, and retreat in others. Five thousand years ago the sea level was probably five or six feet higher than now. The amount of glacier ice was correspondingly less. Yet in the European Alps the ice was 1000 feet thicker than now. At that time the Arctic Ocean in summer may

have been ice-free. There are now temperate regions which are fed in summer by glacier water, as in parts of Switzerland, and as at the little city of Boulder in Colorado; then they were probably arid.

It is thought that the world climate became colder and more stormy about 3000 years ago, and the glaciers began to grow again. Then came another thousand years of glacial retreat, followed by a new advance in the period from the seventeenth to the nineteenth century. This last advance was recorded in Iceland, Scandinavia, and the Alps. During the last century the glaciers have again been diminishing, and the sea level has risen by two or three inches. However, in some regions the glaciers have been changing contrary to the general trend.

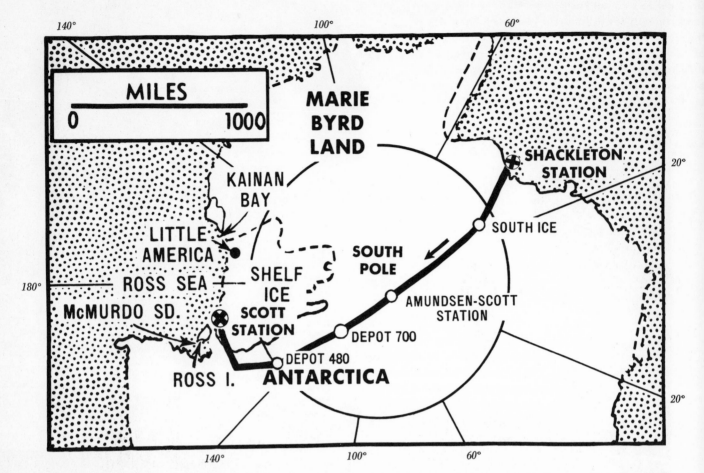

The scientific study of glaciers goes back little more than a century. The science of glaciology took a spurt when the Swedish investigator Ahlmann greatly improved the methods used. In the past 70 years the Greenland ice cap has been visited by many scientific expeditions. The later ones have been much the most productive.

During the IGY special attention was given to the Antarctic ice cap, by many nations. The extensive Asian glaciers were also studied by many Russian IGY expeditions. Some time must pass before the results are properly studied and published, but already several interesting discoveries have been made known. The Antarctic was crossed for the first time from coast to coast by a British Commonwealth Trans-Antarctic team. It visited the U.S. South Pole Station on the way. Along its route this expedition took seismic soundings of the ice thickness. So also did many other expeditions sent out from the IGY Antarctic stations. By such means it was found by a U.S. team that Byrd station, on top of the ice cap, has almost 10,000 feet of ice below it. But Byrd station is about 5,000 feet above sea level. Here, then, there is much more ice than was to be expected. Further exploration must be undertaken to discover whether the ice there rests on an inland sea or a frozen fiord. The depression of the ground below this great thickness of ice may be partly due to the overlying weight. Glaciers do affect the land level; during the last centuries much of Scandinavia has been rising at the rate of about a foot per century—a slow recovery from the depression of the area during the last ice age.

The greatest ice-shelf in the world is that of the Ross Sea. It extends more than 400

The route followed by the British IGY party, led by Dr. (now Sir) Vivian Fuchs, that made the first over-land crossing of the Antarctic continent. They visited the U. S. IGY station at the South Pole in the course of their hazardous journey of 2,100 miles, which they accomplished in 90 days. On the second half of their journey they were supplied by depots set up by a party led by Sir Edmund Hillary.

A U. S. traverse party from the Ellsworth IGY Antarctic Station covered several hundred miles in Edith Ronne Land during the 1957–58 Antarctic summer, making scientific observations along the route. One of their vehicles, a Sno-Cat and its 2½-ton sled carrying food and fuel in drums, broke through the bridge of a crevasse—fortunately narrow. A scientist—rope protected—approaches to examine the situation.

Three members of a U. S. Navy team explore ice formations in an Antarctic ice cave. Many icicles hang from the roof. The men are silhouetted against the glare of a hidden floodlight. They were part of an IGY expedition that remained in the Antarctic through the long winter night.

36378

A skin-diver scientist studies a submerged coral atoll at close quarters.

miles into the great Ross Sea bay, from a point only about 300 miles from the South Pole. Part of the shelf has been found to be over 1000 feet thick, and to be floating above well over 1000 feet of sea water.

Glacial ice can be explored to depths considerably more than 1000 feet by drilling, as well as by artificial ice-quakes. Cores of ice can be drawn out in the drilling tubes. They enable the past history of the ice to be studied. They show the layers added year by year, and thus give some indication of past climate. In a core got from a hole drilled in the Greenland ice cap in 1956, the 1912 layer showed the presence of ash from an Alaskan volcano that erupted in that year. In 1883 there was a great eruption of the volcano Krakatao, in the East Indies. Its ash became spread abroad in the atmosphere, and slowly fell over the whole world. This will be a help in identifying the annual layers in the cores from glaciers in widely separated places. Because there is less snowfall over the Antarctic than over Greenland, this ash-marked layer may be about 150 feet down in the Greenland ice, and perhaps only 60 feet down in the Antarctic.

These are some few of the many ways in which glacier studies are made. Such studies are important for mankind because of the influence of glaciers on the sea level and on world climate and weather. Glaciers are important sources also of water supply and hydroelectric power.

Thick layers of ice store much history of the earth's past. Here T. R. Butkovich, a physicist of the U.S. Army establishment for the study of snow, ice, and permafrost, holds a cylinder of ice that is more than 800 years old. It is the lowest part of a "core" 4 inches in diameter and more than 1300 ft. long. The core was drilled from the Arctic icecap and cut into sections for transport to the laboratory (Wilmette, Illinois), for examination in the "cold room." Trapped in the ice are ancient bacteria—perfectly preserved—and bubbles of air that give atmospheric samples dating back to about the time of the Norman Conquest of England.

The Oceans

The oceans, however, are far more important to mankind than the glaciers. They hold about 99 per cent of the earth's water. They cover 71 per cent of the earth's surface. Their area is 140 million square miles. The Pacific, Alantic, and Indian oceans account for 89 per cent of this area. The Pacific area slightly exceeds the combined area of the Atlantic and Indian oceans.

Past ages have seen great changes in the oceans. Much present land was once under the sea. In the state of Colorado in the U.S., for example, there are 10,000 feet of sediments, slowly deposited under the sea surface during at least three separate periods of submergence. The Grand Canyon of the Colorado river shows a magnificent section of part of such sediments.

The oceans both separate and link the nations. Separation led to differences between their human inhabitants and between their fauna and flora. At times they could mingle by crossing land connections between areas now separated by water.

Explorers and surveyors have mapped the borders of the oceans. The only part of the earth where there is still any appreciable doubt as to where the sea and land join is in the Antarctic.

The art of navigation beyond sight of land slowly developed, as the magnetic compass came into use, and later the ship's chronometer. Until good chronometers became available, differences of longitude at sea had to be estimated by reckoning from the ship's bearings and log. Ocean currents not suspected or not properly allowed for could lead to gross errors of estimated longitude. An example is shown in the first magnetic map of the Atlantic Ocean, published by Edmund Halley, the second Astronomer Royal of England, in 1701 A.D.; it showed the southern tip of America nearly 10° too far west (p. 81). Nowadays mariners keep accurate time from radio time signals: then by star and sun observations they can well determine their position on the globe. Only prolonged cloudy weather can leave uncertainty, which can now sometimes be relieved by long distance radio beams. The gyro-compass supplements or replaces the magnetic compass on some ships. The underwater passage of the U.S. submarine "Nautilus" in 1958, over a course of thousands of miles, shows how largely man has overcome the difficulties of navigation out of sight of the sky.

The sounding lead enabled mariners to measure the depth of the sea, and warned them of the approach to rocks, islands, and coasts. Survey ships plumbed the sea depths systematically, in order to chart the sea bottom. In 1889 a British ship, H.M.S. "Egeria," in this way found that at a point near the Tonga Islands in the southwest Pacific, 24,000 feet of wire had to be let out to touch the bottom. The ship had found a point in one of a number of very deep trenches in the ocean bed. These have since been further explored and partly mapped by the oceanographers of several nations. There is a vast chain of trenches around the main Pacific basin; the lowest depth yet found is about 35,000 feet—seven miles. Such a chasm as the Tonga-Kermadec Trench—in which seven Grand Canyons could be piled, each rising

from the next, and whose length is the distance from New York to Kansas City—is a thing of wonder. The maps of the sea bed, from which also great mountains and mountain chains ascend, are still incomplete. Nowadays sound waves echoed from the sea bed provide a much quicker and more convenient method of plumbing the depth; and man-made explosions set up elastic waves in the water, by which also the nature of the sea bed, below its surface, can be examined. For example, layers of sediment resting on rock can be measured.

A landmark in the history of man's knowledge of the oceans was the expedition of H.M.S. "Challenger," 1872–76. It has been said that the birth of modern oceanography dates from this memorable expedition. Its work was both physical and biological, and its results were published from 1880 to 1895, in 50 large volumes. Since then knowledge of the oceans has progressed apace. But the oceans are so extensive that very much remains to be measured and discovered. The rate of advance is from time to time speeded up by the invention of new instruments. They may make measurements better and more

Two scientists, V. Kitaev (left) and O. Kiselev, members of a U.S.S.R. IGY oceanographic expedition, are here shown in a submerged laboratory. They are making a moving film of the sea bed, which they illuminate with a strong beam of light. On the right is a photograph of the ocean bottom at a depth of 50 fathoms, showing starfish, and small sea plants growing vertically.

quickly than did the earlier instruments, or measurements that previously could not be made at all.

The International Geophysical Year was a period of intense oceanographic effort, by many nations. They worked separately or in conjunction, on an agreed program. Observations of many kinds, including biological, were made on several voyages by special vessels. Some vessels on other missions, for example to take expeditions to the Antarctic, also made ocean observations. In addition, instruments were placed on many coasts and islands, particularly to measure sea level and its tidal and other changes. These sea level instruments were surveyed by precise leveling.

Some of the sea level recorders are designed to register long sea waves. These are of interest to oceanographers in themselves; they are also of interest because in many cases they come from regions of stormy weather, perhaps hundreds of miles away.

They may be of value to weather science as a means of locating such storm areas, in regions where there is no on-the-spot weather record. These long waves are also linked with small weak earthquake waves—microseisms—which start from the stormy règion owing to the varying sea pressure on the bottom, as big waves roll overhead. Sometimes destructive long waves are set up on the ocean by real earthquakes under the ocean.

Oceanographers study the ocean water itself in numerous ways—particularly its temperature, its salt content, and its content of oxygen and carbon dioxide and other materials, at different depths. They also wish to know the sea currents, not only at the surface but also below the surface.

Recently a new electrical method invented in the U.S. has made measurement of the salinity much easier and quicker. Another new electrical instrument has been devised to measure the ocean currents from a ship. As the ship will be partly drifting with the

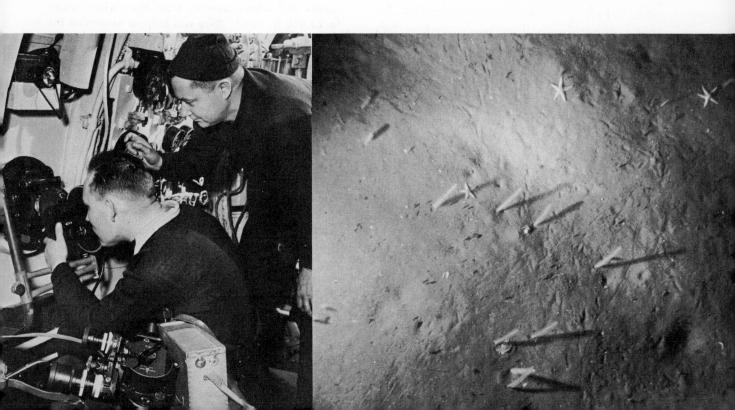

water this is not easy to do. The principle used is that the motion of the water relative to the earth's magnetism induces an electric field, which can be measured by electrodes hung from the ship. One discovery obtained with this instrument relates to the Gulf Stream. This flows from the equator along the east coast of South and North America, and then crosses the Atlantic to Europe, whose climate it much improves. Observers have found that the Gulf Stream can change its course considerably in a week or two. Sometimes it swerves aside and then the bend gets cut off, as happens more slowly with rivers on land.

The oceanographic program laid stress on the measurement of deep sea currents. Sometimes there are countercurrents beneath or near the main surface currents. Very little is yet known about the deep movements. They are important to weather forecasting because they exchange heat between lower and higher latitudes. They also affect the fertility of the oceans, and consequently our food supply, by producing exchanges between mineral-rich deep water and surface water.

Oceanographer William A. Metcalf lowers a "Nansen" bottle from the "Crawford," one of the research vessels of the Woods Hole Oceanographic Institution, Massachusetts. The bottle is named after the great Norwegian oceanographer and humanitarian. The "Crawford," during a two-month IGY cruise in the Caribbean Sea and Atlantic Ocean, obtained more than 2,000 temperature measurements and water samples from the surface down to 23,000 ft. depth. They will help to determine the circulation in the Atlantic and the "age" of the deep Caribbean water.

The picture opposite shows the neutral buoyancy float devised by Dr. J. C. Swallow of the British National Institute of Oceanography. It is lying on the deck of a research vessel. At the left-hand end is the nickel scroll transducer—the sound transmitter. Weighted so as to float at any desired depth, it stays vertical and drifts freely with the subsurface currents. Its introduction has greatly simplified the study of the movements of the ocean water at different depths.

New ways of measuring deep sea currents were developed and extensively used during the IGY. The movement of the survey vessels was determined by radar relative to buoys fixed by taut wires to anchors in the sea bottom. Current meters were hung from the ship at various depths, to determine the deep sea current speed and direction. The deep sea currents were also measured by free-floating sea anchors.

Yet another important device for measuring deep sea currents is the neutral buoyancy float. This device, weighing about 22 lbs., consists of two aluminum tubes nearly 9 feet long tied side by side: one contains batteries and instruments, the other is hollow but can be suitably weighted to make the device stay at any desired depth down to five miles. Attached below the two tubes is a sound transmitter. By weighted hydrophones hung from the two ends of a nearby survey vessel, the relative position of the float can be measured by swinging the ship round. The ship's position is measured relative to an anchored buoy, whose own slight drift is checked by sounding over small but recognizable features of the sea bed.

The neutral buoyancy float has been used in the Atlantic in joint U.S.–U.K. oceanographic surveys, and in the Pacific in the Scripps Oceanographic Institution surveys there. Most interesting results have been obtained, and this device seems likely to play an important future part in oceanography. In trials of the method in 1955, in the sea 3 miles deep west of Portugal, at a depth of about 1800 feet, the float drifted at the rate of 1.3 miles per day in the direction 30° north of west. Its path was looped twice daily by tidal currents, so that these also were determined. In the same region, 10 days earlier, a deeper float, at about 3000 feet, drifted at 3 miles a day in the direction 20° south of west; this float did not show tidal deviations.

The U.K. Royal Research vessel "Discovery II" re-examined this region west of Oporto, in May to July 1958, using several floats at different depths and positions. The region was chosen as having a flat sea floor and likely to have fairly weak currents. Measurements were made at depths from nearly 1 to 2.5 miles. The most interesting feature of the results was that in a small horizontal distance—of the order of 20 to 30 miles—

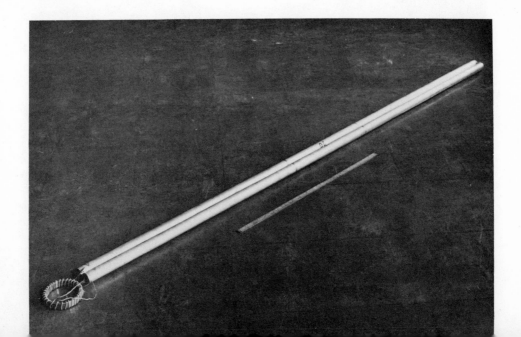

Not only ice (page 34) but also the sea bed is examined by taking cylindrical samples called cores. The ice cores are got by drilling. The sea bed is softer and less accessible. But oceanographers have devised effective methods to obtain cores. Here the coring apparatus is being lowered from the side of the "Vema," research vessel of the Lamont Geological Observatory of Columbia University, New York. The apparatus consists of a long pipe with a heavy weight on top. At about 12–15 ft. from the bottom, a small trigger releases the weighted pipe, which sinks into the sediments. The pipe is hauled back to the ship and the core is removed for analysis. When the magnetism of the sediments is to be measured, a device attached to the pipe enables the north side of the core to be identified.

there are variations of speed by a factor of 10, at the same depth; and the speed and direction may change notably in a week or so. Thus there is what may be called "water weather" deep in the ocean. If such conditions occur generally it is going to be difficult to estimate average ocean currents at different depths, and the future labors of oceanographers will be greatly increased.

The neutral buoyancy floats were also used in a (1957) joint U.K.–U.S. program in the Gulf Stream off South Carolina, in the region of the Florida current. The surface current there is strong, usually more than 100 miles per day. Seven floats at depths of 2700 to 3000 yards showed southward or south-westward currents of 1.5 to 15 miles per day. An ingenious method was used to measure the current at only half a yard above the sea bed, at 3500 yards depth: underwater photographs were taken of a ball held down by a string. This measurement also showed a southward current of about 2.5 miles a day.

During the IGY, vessels of the Scripps Institution and the U.S. Fish and Wildlife Service made a remarkable discovery of a great submarine river that flows for at least 3500 miles near the equator in the Pacific. The current is 250 miles wide and from 100 to 800 feet below the surface. It is one of the great oceanographic discoveries of our time, comparable with the discovery of jet streams in the upper atmosphere. The current flows eastward at about 27 miles per day and is sandwiched between two slow westward currents, one at the surface—recall the Kon-Tiki voyage—and the other below 800 feet. The current disperses near the Galapagos Islands (89°W). The volume of the flow is comparable with that of the Gulf Stream or a thousand Mississippis.

These are but a few first-fruits of the International Geophysical Year in the study of the solid earth and the oceans.

Meteorologists hope that future earth satellites will survey the distribution of clouds over the earth and transmit the information to the weather offices. Here is an artist's conception of the kind of picture that will thus be obtained from a satellite 4,000 miles above Amarillo, Texas. Clouds reflect much of the sunlight and thus modify the air and land temperature distribution over the earth (see also page 45).

THE ATMOSPHERE

The atmosphere is the breath of life to every one of us. Though it is invisible, our senses tell us whether it is warm or cold, calm or windy, dry or moist. But the scientific study of the atmosphere had to wait for the invention of instruments that could measure its properties. The wind vane, giving the direction of the wind, was one of the earliest of these instruments. Then came the barometer and thermometer, already in the seventeenth century, and later the anemometer to measure the wind speed, and the hygrometer or wet and dry bulb thermometers to measure its humidity.

Gradually, decade by decade, century by century, the use of such instruments in many places gave us a knowledge of the distribution of pressure, temperature, wind and humidity over the earth—though with many gaps. An early effort to fill in one of the areas of gap was the first International Polar Year, 1882–83, when several nations joined to observe the weather elements over the Arctic on a common plan. The International Geophysical Year is a similar effort which includes the study of the Antarctic, to fill an even greater gap in our knowledge of the properties of the atmosphere.

The knowledge thus gained is represented on special world maps to be found in physical atlases—maps of the world distribution of air temperature, pressure, wind, humidity — not only the annual average values, but also seasonal or even monthly means. These are most reliable over the land. It is harder to get such reliable measurements over the oceans, especially for the parts less frequented by ships.

Already three hundred years ago there was interest in knowing not only how pressure and temperature varied at the ground level, but also in height. The great geometer Pascal realized that the barometer measures the weight of overlying air, and that as one ascends, the barometer reading must decrease. He proved this by observations on a high mountain. Mountain observations also showed that in general the temperature gets less as one ascends. Dalton, one of the fathers of chemistry, thought that the composition of the air, which he helped to study, must change with height, and that he had verified this by mountain observations. Later studies showed that his observations were incorrect, and it is now known that the air at ground level, and as far as balloons can reach, has great constancy of composition all over the earth. The only variations of composition of the air at the ground affect small constituents like water vapor, ozone and carbon dioxide and radon. These are constituents that can undergo physical or chemical changes—unlike most of the gases of the air, especially the major constituents nitrogen and oxygen. Some of the rarer constituents of the air were not discovered till the present century.

Near the end of the nineteenth century the variation of temperature in the atmosphere with height began to be actively studied by means of kites. In this way it was found by a Frenchman, De Bort, that the air does not continue to get colder the higher up we go, beyond a level of about 6 or 7 miles. Above that level—which came to be called the tropopause—the temperature remained constant, or sometimes even increased slightly, as one went higher. The lower region of upward decreasing temperature was called the troposphere, and the upper region, the stratosphere. Similar observations, which later came to be made not by kites but by small balloons carrying very light recording instruments, were made in other parts of the globe. It was thus found that the tropopause is higher in low latitudes than in temperate and polar latitudes. Its height over the equator is about 12 miles, and in the Arctic it is only about 5 miles. But the average rate of decrease of temperature with height, about 17°F per mile, is much the same at all latitudes. Hence although the ground temperature at the equator exceeds that in the Arctic, the tropopause temperature is lowest at the equator, about —110°F. About a quarter century ago a great advance in the explora-

The Nike-Cajun rocket, here shown on its launcher, on Guam Island, is an economical high-altitude research rocket that proved very successful during the IGY. It could be and was launched both on land and on shipboard; the launching rail can be tilted up to the vertical or any desired angle. The rocket can carry a payload of about fifty pounds to heights of one hundred miles or more. The rocket here shown was used to measure the wind and temperature in the upper atmosphere, by means of the grenade experiment developed jointly by the University of Michigan and the Signal Corps (see also p. 58).

This picture is a composite made from five photographs taken by a rocket-borne camera on March 7, 1947. It shows the cloud distribution over a large area with its center near White Sands, New Mexico, whence the rocket was launched. The rocket was a German V-2, made for use late in World War II. The U. S. Army captured many of these rockets and brought them to the USA. Many of them were used for purely scientific purposes, especially for studies of the upper atmosphere.

tion of the atmosphere in height was made by adding radio transmitters to the measuring instruments, which could thus signal their measurements to the ground. This gave their results immediately, whereas previously the instruments had to be found before their readings could be known; as they might drift far from the launching point, there was at least delay in getting the results, and they might not be got at all if the instruments and balloon fell into the sea or were not found.

These improvements in the exploration of the atmosphere came in time to be used during the second polar year, 1932–33, when the Arctic atmosphere was first studied up to the then attainable heights of about 6 miles. Over the oceans such measurements required greater organization, and were not regularly made till after World War II. Then a few weather ships were equipped and stationed at places in the north Atlantic Ocean, by cooperation between some of the European and North American nations. Thus, daily observations of the upper atmosphere began to be made at many places on the earth, including the Atlantic Ocean. The growth of travel by air created a need for high-level measurements of wind, as well as of pressure and temperature and humidity.

The increasing height at which aircraft fly gave an incentive to explore the atmosphere to ever higher levels. Better balloons capable of rising to a height of 20 miles were developed to carry instruments to measure pressure and temperature and to reflect radar signals to give the wind speed and direction. During and soon after World War II it became clear that there were surprising features of the upper air that had been quite unex-

pected. Among these were the jet streams—meandering rivers of air flowing eastward with great speed in middle latitudes, and fluctuating much in course and speed during only a few days. The tropopause was found to be less simple than had been supposed; it was broken in the latitudes of the jet streams, where there were at times two tropopauses at different levels.

After World War II the exploration of the atmosphere was pushed to still higher levels by rockets. Much developed during the war for destructive purposes, they came to be of great service in the scientific investigation of the upper atmosphere. In this work the physicists and engineers of the United States gave

During the IGY, expeditions and ships visited many regions where few or no scientific observations had hitherto been made. The opportunities were taken to make observations additional to those that were the main purpose of the expedition. Here wind observations are being taken by Mr. Bob Menzies, a member of the Kenya IGY glaciological expedition (pp. 28, 29), on the Lewis Glacier of Mount Kenya. The instrument used is a portable anemometer. At the top of the pole are the cups that are turned by the wind. The number of turns they have made is shown by the counters in the glass-windowed box below. The turns made are noted at two times; this gives the speed of the wind.

a lead, both in devising the necessary instruments to measure and signal the air properties met as the rocket sped through the air, and also in developing the rockets themselves.

The rocket measurements partly confirmed, and partly corrected and extended, several inferences that had been made about the properties of the upper air, on the basis of ground level observations of different kinds. These included the observation of sound waves reflected downwards from heights of 20 miles or so, from gunfire or explosions at distances of 60 or more miles: also the observation of meteor trails, mostly at 40 to 60 miles height.

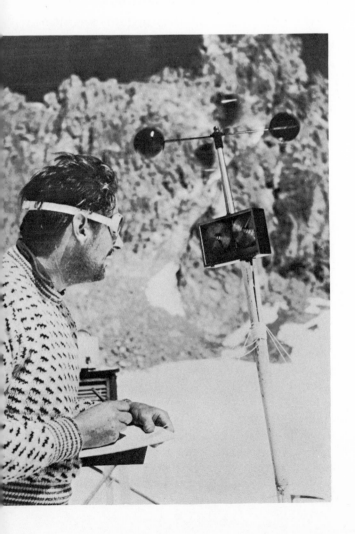

Thus we now know that as we ascend above the tropopause we reach a layer where the temperature in middle latitudes begins to increase again from the low values attained in the stratosphere. At about 30 miles height it has risen to a maximum value of about 30°F. From there it declines again to another minimum, at about 50 miles height; the exact minimum temperature is not yet certain, but it may be −135°F or even less. The air there is even colder than at the tropopause above the equator—very surprisingly, one of the coldest regions on our planet. Above 50 miles height the temperature increases upwards again, as far as our observations have yet been carried out, to about 200 miles up.

Such rocket observations cannot be made easily at any chosen place. They require ground installation, and a restricted area where safety precautions can be taken. Special testing stations developed mainly for military needs are mostly used. However, simpler rockets called rockoons have been devised and used, especially at sea, where safety restrictions are easier; they are launched from balloons at a height of about 20 miles. Thus, they start above the main mass of the atmosphere, and require less power and are less weighty and expensive.

The extension of the study of the atmosphere was one of the principal objectives of the IGY. Weather observations by ground instruments and by meteorological balloons were already made very extensively over the globe before the IGY began; but there were many gaps in the area covered and great differences in the degree of cover in different parts of the world. The IGY intensified the previous types of weather observation even in the most advanced countries, and led to much improvement of the observations in the countries that are less active scientifically. The volume of weather observations that was collected during the IGY is truly prodigious. In the planning of this work the World Meteorological Organization (WMO) has cooperated with the IGY organization. The WMO is a governmental organization, a branch of the Economic and Social Organ (ECOSOC) of the United Nations Organization. About 100 meteorological services in lands all over the earth are linked with it. The WMO collected all the IGY meteorological observations, and will reproduce them on microcards in highly condensed form. A complete set of the weather data on such cards will be purchasable for just under $6000.

For half a century or more the weather services of different countries have issued forecasts of the coming weather during the following day or days. Despite the great growth of observations available to them, not only at ground level but also up to heights of 10 to 20 miles, and despite the growth of a complex organization for collecting these observations quickly by teletype from a large part of the earth, the progress of weather prediction has been less than had earlier been hoped. The more the atmosphere is observed and studied, the clearer it becomes that it is an extremely complicated system. Every scientist believes that the atmosphere works according to fixed physical laws. We believe that if we knew enough about its laws and about its state at one particular instant, and if we knew sufficiently the laws and the state of the oceans also at that instant—because the oceans and atmosphere greatly affect each other — it should be possible to foretell the

later course of their changes, with fair accuracy — assuming that the sun's radiation is constant. To make such forecasts from such complete data for the atmosphere and oceans, we should need to know not only the physical laws governing them, but also we should need great powers of rapid calculation. About forty years ago a British meteorologist named Richardson published a book entitled *Weather Prediction by Numerical Process*. He added to his book, as a fantasy of the future, a description of a world office into which weather data were fed daily by cable or radio from all over the globe, and in which troops of computers were engaged in calculating as fast as they could, how the weather would change. His dream was that a time might come when their calculations could predict the development of the actual weather, with a sufficient time margin for the forecasts to be useful. He

Radar now serves weathermen in more than one way. Balloons are launched from which a reflecting device is hung. A transmitter station sends radar beams which are echoed back from the reflector. This determines the direction and distance to the balloon. Its motion can thus be followed, giving the wind direction and speed at that level in the atmosphere. This picture illustrates another meteorological use of radar of an unusual kind. The bowl, situated near Moscow, is excavated in the ground, and lined with reflecting material. It forms a giant reflecting mirror for radio waves. These are generated in the transmitter suspended over the bowl. After being reflected upward by the bowl, they are echoed back from cloud formations over a considerable area around. The bowl then reflects them back to a receiver alongside the transmitter, giving a record of the extent and structure of the clouds.

Guest meteorologists from other countries, including Russia, worked with U. S. meteorologists at the central Antarctic weather station at Little America. Similarly, a U. S. meteorologist worked at one of the U.S.S.R. stations. Here an Austrian meteorologist, Dr. Herfried Hoinkes, examines an anemometer—to record the wind speed—at the Little America station.

put into his book all he knew about the world weather on a certain day, and worked out — not during hours or even days, but during weeks or months — what it would be on the following day. His comparison with the actual records of the weather on that day showed only a moderate degree of success; this was to be expected, as his data were very incomplete.

Since that time there has been an astonishing development in calculating machines. Electronic machines of several different kinds have been devised that can speed up calculation far beyond anything that Richardson could have foreseen when he wrote his book. His dream has approached decidedly nearer to becoming a reality. Already meteorologists in this and other countries have been trying their prentice hands at weather prediction by numerical calculation, with encouraging success. But these are still only the first steps towards the goal. The earth is so extensive that to get the necessary observations from all over the globe is beyond our present powers, instrumental, financial, and organizational. The goal of reliable prediction beyond a day or two seems still somewhat remote. But the great IGY extension of weather observation will give the weather scientists better data now than they could have thought of having, even as recently as ten years ago. They will be able to apply their powers of computation to the observations with more hope and confidence than before, because they will be so much more complete. Earth satellites may greatly help the weather scientists in the future by giving information about the worldwide distribution of clouds.

However, there will still be large gaps in the IGY information, and especially as regards the oceans. At present this is inevitable, though a time may come when automatic recording instruments, moored at many ocean points, will signal observations to a weather central office, probably through intermediate reception and transmission stations, perhaps likewise automatic. The observations may even come from balloons they have launched. Alternatively, there may be an extension of the aircraft flights now made regularly in some regions, to measure and report the properties of the air along their course.

During the IGY special provisions were included in the plans, to help toward a better scientific understanding of weather processes. The atmosphere is a great engine, powered by the solar radiation that falls on it. The solar energy is all radiated away again — the earth remains at substantially a constant temperature. But more radiation is received

The speed of the wind at different levels in the air is determined by radar echoes from reflectors suspended by balloons. These rise to and float at predetermined heights. This method is called rawin (shortened from radar-wind). In the Antarctic the radar transmitter and receiver are housed in a dome. Such a dome, at the U. S. Byrd Station, Antarctica, is being cleared of snow by meteorologist Norbert F. Helfert during a snowstorm (see also pp. 52, 71).

A general view of the U. S. Byrd IGY Station at 80° S, 120° W, in October 1957, at the end of a winter of drifting snow. On the left is an antenna mast for radio communications, then the rawin dome shown on pp. 51, 71. Stove flues appear above the snow, just right of center; to the right, a mast carrying a wind vane (electrically recording), the boom of a Caterpillar tractor, and an auroral observatory located on top of a tower. Though the snow accumulation was less than 2 ft. in the year, snow drifts piled up against the buildings and other obstacles.

at low latitudes that is radiated away from them, and vice versa at high latitudes. Thus, there must be a transport of energy from low latitudes to high by movement of air in a great general circulation. The ocean currents also transport heat between different regions of the globe and exchange heat with the atmosphere. The jet streams must be an important feature of the mechanism of this atmospheric engine. Momentum also, and water, are exchanged between different latitudes and levels. To understand these processes better, it was desirable to have as complete weather observations as possible along certain meridians stretching as fully as geography permits from pole to pole. The best observed meridian extends along the east coast of North America and down the west coast of South America. A less completely observed meridian crosses Europe and Africa, and another goes across Asia to Antarctica. Observations along certain belts of latitude were also organized. The study of the passage of heat and other atmospheric properties across these meridians and belts will enable the weather scientists to learn much about the transport processes in the atmosphere.

Another feature of the weather program was the stepping up of the intensity of observation — for example, of the number of balloons launched per day, and the height to which they go — in certain special periods. There was a special interval of ten days in each quarter-year, and three or more special days each month. On these days and intervals the observations were more complete — at a level of frequency and altitude beyond what could at present be achieved regularly on every day of the 18 months of the IGY.

The full study of the great mass of weather data thus obtained will take a considerable time. But already much new knowledge is available, especially for the Antarctic — the least well explored region of the globe.

By agreement in 1955 between the nations that sent IGY expeditions to the Antarctic, a Weather Central station was established at the U.S. Little America station. The Central had the task of collecting weather reports from all Antarctic stations, from nearby ships and aircraft, and from land traverse parties. It made four ground-level synoptic weather charts for the Antarctic each day, and also synoptic charts for three higher levels once daily, over the region for which data were available. The latter charts gave temperature and wind at a definite pressure level. Analyses and 24-hour weather outlooks were also issued, and the individual IGY stations used these as a basis for their local weather forecasts. The Central was staffed by four U.S. meteorologists and one each from the Argentine and the U.S.S.R. Weekly discussions on Antarctic meteorology were held, and 10-day and monthly weather charts were prepared. All this represents a most notable advance in the progress of Antarctic meteorology, and should show to what extent the weather of the Southern Hemisphere as a whole is influenced by conditions on the Antarctic continent.

At the U.S. station at the South Pole record low temperatures were registered on more than one occasion. The lowest so far was −102°F. on September 17, 1957. The previous coldest spot on the earth's surface was a place in northeast Siberia, where in February 1933 the thermometer fell to −90°F. The South Pole station is nearly 10,000 feet above sea level. In reporting this record low temperature, the U.S. IGY *Bulletin* (No. 5, p. 6) remarked that even lower temperatures might be recorded at the "Pole of Inaccessibility," the center of the Antarctic continent, which is further from the coast than the South Pole, and 4000 to 5000 feet higher. The Russians hope to set up an IGY station at that "Pole," but during the first part of the program this was not possible. The nearest of their stations was about 425 miles from it (78°24′S, 87°35′E). Its elevation was about 12,100 feet; there, during the 1958 Antarctic winter (our summer), a new record low temperature of −114°F. was registered. At such a temperature metal loses its strength, rubber breaks, and diesel fluid becomes viscous and thick, like honey.

At the South Pole, and at many other places in the Antarctic and Arctic, there is a pronounced temperature inversion at times of extreme cold at the ground. At the South Pole on the record occasion mentioned, the temperature was 27°F. higher at a height of only 30 feet above the surface, and at 1400 feet it was 72° higher. Above this level the temperature diminished, as usual, with increasing height.

In the Arctic, extreme low temperatures have been recorded in the past at some land stations—for example, −81°F. at Snag Airport, Yukon Territory, Canada in February 1947, and −87° at a French station in Greenland, near the top of the ice cap, in February 1950. At the North Pole the lowest temperature is not likely to be much less than −60°, because it is in the midst of a sea where the ice thickness averages less than 15 feet, so that heat can be conducted to the air from the deep and relatively warm sea water below.

The mean wind speed at the South Pole during the first IGY winter was 16 miles per hour, with gusts up to 53 mph. There were only 25 hours of calm during the entire winter. Thus the climate there is exceptionally severe. A U.S.S.R. oversnow trail party, during the 1957-58 summer (our winter) met winds of 134 miles per hour, at a point 200 miles west of the main Soviet base at Mirny, on the Queen Mary coast in east Antarctica.

A more general advance in weather observation during the year was a great extension of measures of solar radiation and of ozone, both at the ground and at heights up to about 12 miles. Pressure, temperature, and wind will be more widely known up to 20 miles. The information will be of much value in theoretical studies of world weather.

During the IGY the upper atmosphere was intensively studied by means of instruments of many kinds carried on rockets. A great part in this program was played by rockoons —rockets carried up to a height of 15 to 20 miles by balloons and launched from that height by signals from ground level. Rockoons can conveniently be dispatched from shipboard. Here the balloon for a rockoon launch is being inflated with helium on the deck of USS "Glacier" in the Antarctic. The rocket (not shown) carried aloft instruments to measure the intensity of cosmic rays at different heights in the atmosphere (see p. 65).

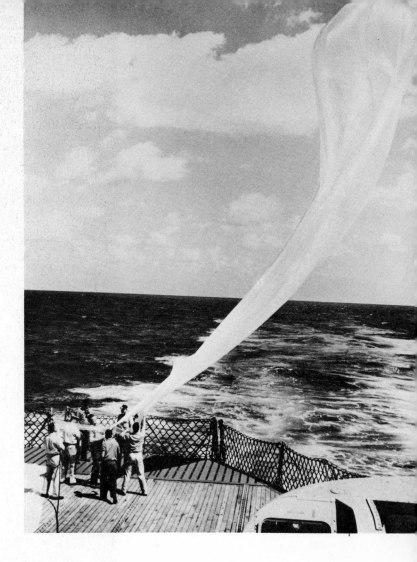

The Upper Atmosphere

The considerable difference between the height and temperature at the equatorial tropopause as compared with the polar tropopause makes it likely that also at still greater heights in the upper atmosphere there will be important differences depending on latitude.

The available rocket data for temperature in the U.S. mainly refer to White Sands, New Mexico (at latitude 33°N.). There the observations cover a period of several years. They have been made by several different groups and by several different methods. In 1952 a summary of the results was published by the U.S. Upper Atmosphere Research Rocket Panel, in the *Physical Review*. Temperature height curves obtained by different groups showed differences amounting at some heights (for example, 47 miles) to over 75°F. It is still not clear how far the differences correspond to seasonal and irregular variations of the true temperature, or to what extent the measurements are affected by systematic errors. The measurements are very difficult, because of the speed with which the rocket traverses the air, and for other reasons. We may expect a greater variability of conditions in the upper atmosphere than near the ground, for several reasons—particularly because the upper air is so much less dense, and

The U. S. rocket research program for the IGY used several different kinds of rockets (including rockoons). The largest were of a type called Aerobee-Hi, of which 30 were launched. It was developed from an earlier model, the Aerobee. Both were "boosted," that is, assisted in the first stages of their flight by an auxiliary rocket. This used a solid propellant. It fell away after 2½ seconds. The main rocket was propelled by liquid fuel —red fuming nitric acid and aniline-alcohol mixture. The Aerobee-Hi was specially designed for upper atmospheric research. It can carry a payload of 68 kilograms (about 150 lb.) into the F region of the ionosphere—over 180 miles.

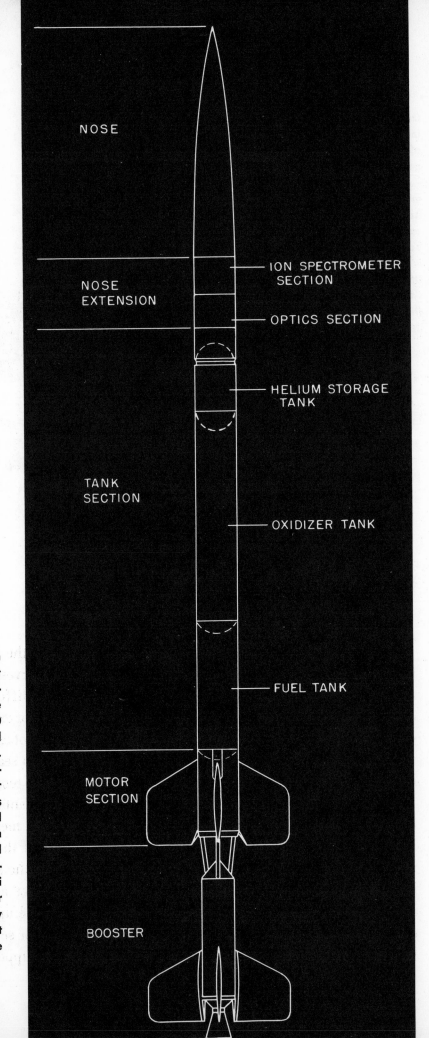

NOSE

NOSE EXTENSION

TANK SECTION

MOTOR SECTION

BOOSTER

ION SPECTROMETER SECTION

OPTICS SECTION

HELIUM STORAGE TANK

OXIDIZER TANK

FUEL TANK

because the solar radiations absorbed there (which are of short wave length, in the ultra-violet) have a much greater proportional variability than has the visible radiation that mostly reaches the ground and is absorbed there. Hence if the temperature variations are greater, and more irregular, a longer series of measurements is needed to get good averages and to distinguish the fairly regular seasonal changes from those that are irregular and dependent on changes in the intrinsic state of the sun.

The U.S. IGY rocket program for the study of the upper atmosphere was very ample. During the first 12 months of the 18 months, no less than 116 rockets were launched under this program. The preliminary results were given in a comprehensive report presented by the U.S. delegation to the last great IGY conference held during the Year. It was at Moscow in July–August 1958. To find how the upper atmospheric conditions vary with latitude, the launchings were made over a range extending from 75° north to 72° south. Sixty-two rockets were launched from land stations—6 from New Mexico (White Sands and Holloman); 15 from San Nicolas Island, California (34°11′N, 119°05′W); and by the co-operative courtesy of the Canadian government, 41 from Fort Churchill (58°46′N, 94°10′W), on the shores of Hudson's Bay. The other 54 were rockoons, launched from ships, between latitudes 75° north and 72° south.

The measurements made with these rockets were very varied. The rockoons were all devoted to cosmic rays, the aurora, and the magnetic field. Those launched from New Mexico and San Nicolas Island were for the measurement of these quantities, and also water vapor, micrometeorites, airglow, and charge density.

Only at Fort Churchill were the structural properties of the upper atmosphere studied—pressure, density, and temperature. Out of 48 rockets fired there, including 7 pre-IGY rockets, 26 included these measurements, and no less than 21 were satisfactory, despite the unusual conditions there. They were made in October and November 1956, and July-September and December 1957, and in March 1958. The results as yet are provisional, and at present are given mainly in terms of density rather than of temperature or pressure.

One definite statement was that at 50 miles height the summer temperature is −162°F.; this measurement was made in July 1957. This is within the range of values given for that level by the U.S.S.R. rockets, presumably in a somewhat similar latitude. Another statement about the Fort Churchill upper air temperatures was that for levels between 20 and 55 miles they appear to be definitely lower at most seasons than at lower latitudes —presumably meaning at White Sands. However, another report states that at Fort Churchill, between 20 and 28 miles, the summer temperatures are significantly higher than at White Sands.

One ingenious and successful method of measuring the temperature of the high atmosphere depends on the acceleration of a sphere ejected from a rocket, and falling freely. Its acceleration is less than that of gravity because of the air resistance. By measuring the acceleration the air density can be inferred, and hence the temperature. At first this method was applied using a large sphere that

The Nike-Cajun rocket is here shown tilted upward on its launching rail. The lower part is the Nike rocket, the upper is the second-stage Cajun that carries the payload. Solid propellants are used in both. The simplicity of this rocket and its launching system enable it to be handled by a small crew, and launched from a ship as well as from land. The first Nike-Cajun was launched at Wallops Island, Virginia, in July 1956. Several different types of measurement were made using these rockets, during the IGY (see p. 44).

was inflated automatically when outside the rocket. Later, a smaller sphere of 7 inches diameter, containing a delicate accelerometer, became the standard form used in this experiment. Thirteen successful flights using such spheres have so far been made, in latitudes from 39°N to 66°N; five of these were launched at Fort Churchill. The results are as yet only partly worked out. It is very satisfactory that the Fort Churchill winter flights gave temperature distributions agreeing well with those obtained from a quite different method using grenades. The graphs (p. 60) of the Fort Churchill measurements with the falling spheres show that two flights made within four days in January 1958 gave height distributions of temperature which differed from each other by almost as much as that between the distributions found in two flights at latitudes 38° and 66°. This is an illustration of the considerable irregular variability of the atmosphere at the levels concerned. The falling sphere measurements were made up to a height of 55 miles.

I think we must regard these results as an important but still only partial advance towards a world survey of the structure of the upper atmosphere. The measurements will need to be continued over a period of years, with improving instruments and methods, if we are to get a proper understanding of the world weather in the atmosphere up to 50 miles height.

The hotter the air, the more it is spread out in height, and the more slowly does the density diminish with height. Measurements of the density at about 125 miles have been made both by rockets and by inference from the changing orbits of satellites, as well as by

This small sphere, released from the nose cone of a Nike-Cajun rocket, was used during the IGY to measure density and temperature in the upper atmosphere. It is ejected from the rocket at 35 miles height on the upward flight. It coasts up to 100 miles and then falls. It contains an ingenious device (an accelerometer) to measure its downward acceleration, and telemetering equipment to transmit the record to the ground. The device is effective from 60 miles height downward.

inference from radio measurements of the ionosphere; in 1951 a density measurement made at White Sands gave a value 10 million million times less than that of water. Determinations made at the Smithsonian Astrophysical Observatory, Harvard, on three satellites, gave values about five times as great. Radio studies of the satellite signals made at Cambridge, England, gave a value about three times that for White Sands. These results seem to indicate that the air about that level is hotter than had previously been supposed. However, some Fort Churchill measurements made in November 1956 gave a density only about a third of that for White Sands, and a summer day measurement on July 29, 1957, gave a density agreeing well with that at White Sands. Until we have more measurements and can know how variable is the density at those levels, in different latitudes, we cannot be certain about the temperature and structure of the atmosphere at those great heights.

The density depends not only on the temperature and pressure, but also on the composition of the atmosphere. Before the International Geophysical Year a series of studies of the composition of the atmosphere had been made by one of the University of Michigan groups, whose rockets took samples of air at heights up to 66 miles. They indicated that below 37 miles the air is uniformly mixed, despite the tendency for the lighter gases in the air to rise above the heavier ones, as Dalton had foreseen. This is because of the turbulence of the air, connected with variable winds, and upward and downward movements. But above 37 miles evidence of settling out was found — helium, one of the lightest gases, was rather more abundant, and argon, one of the heavier ones, was less so.

At Fort Churchill the composition was studied otherwise from three Aerobee-Hi rockets (p. 56). Each carried a radio-frequency mass spectrometer. They confirm the White Sands results in showing a decrease of argon relative to nitrogen, though only above 62 to 75 miles. At 100 miles height the amount of argon to nitrogen was reduced by a factor of four or five. These results come from rockets fired in November 1956 and February and March 1958.

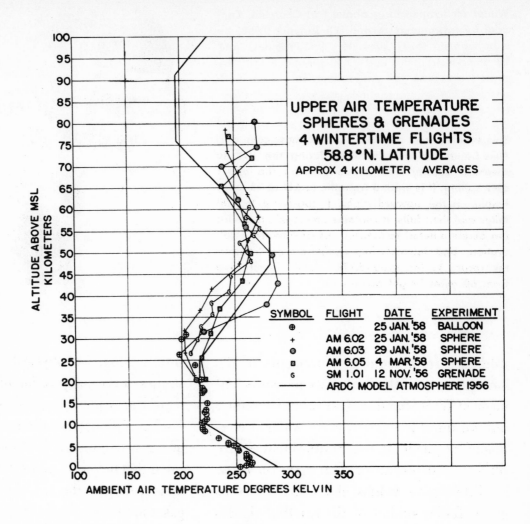

UPPER AIR TEMPERATURE
SPHERES & GRENADES
4 WINTERTIME FLIGHTS
58.8°N. LATITUDE
APPROX 4 KILOMETER AVERAGES

SYMBOL	FLIGHT	DATE	EXPERIMENT
⊕		25 JAN.'58	BALLOON
+	AM 6.02	25 JAN.'58	SPHERE
⊙	AM 6.03	29 JAN.'58	SPHERE
⊡	AM 6.05	4 MAR.'58	SPHERE
∽	SM 1.01	12 NOV.'56	GRENADE
⎯⎯	ARDC MODEL ATMOSPHERE 1956		

ALTITUDE ABOVE MSL KILOMETERS

AMBIENT AIR TEMPERATURE DEGREES KELVIN

Winds in the Upper Atmosphere

The Fort Churchill rocket program included a series of ten rockets carrying means of measuring the wind at levels from 16 to 60 miles. They were launched successfully in summer and winter, and both by day and night. Grenades were ejected from the rocket at successive heights. They exploded outside the rocket, and the time of each explosion was accurately measured. A network of sound recorders on the ground measured the times and directions of reception of the sound waves from the explosions. From these measurements it was possible to calculate both the air temperature and the wind at each height. The method is applicable only below about 60 miles height.

Winter air temperatures above Fort Churchill, Canada, by instruments carried (25 January 1958) by a balloon up to 31 kilometers (= 19 miles), and by other instruments carried to greater heights by rockets, in 1958 (by the falling sphere method) and in 1956 (by the grenade method). Great differences in temperature were shown above 20 miles between 25 and 29 January. The 1956 measurements, up to 60 km, show fair agreement with those of 25 January and 6 March. At 80 km (50 miles) the air above Fort Churchill is much hotter than certain "model" atmospheric calculations indicated. Temperatures in degrees Kelvin are Centigrade temperatures plus 273.

Similar measurements were made at White Sands between 1950 and 1953. In both cases, in summer the winds were toward the west, and in winter toward the east. The wind speed was less in summer than in winter, the difference being more at Fort Churchill than at White Sands. The greatest speeds both at White Sands and Churchill were at levels between about 30 and 40 miles. At both places the maximum speed registered was in November — 200 miles per hour at White Sands, 330 at Churchill, in both cases at about 35 miles height and eastward. These enormous speeds are fully credited by the rocket experts responsible for the flights. In summer, speeds up to 170 miles per hour were measured at White Sands, and also at Churchill, but in general the Churchill summer speeds were decidedly less than at White Sands. In both places irregular variations of temperature and wind were found, more particularly at Churchill.

These observations are of great interest, and confirm measurements of meteor trails and of high night clouds (50 miles high) in showing very high wind speeds at those levels. They deserve the attention of the dynamical meteorologists who are experienced in the study of winds, pressure, and temperature at much lower levels.

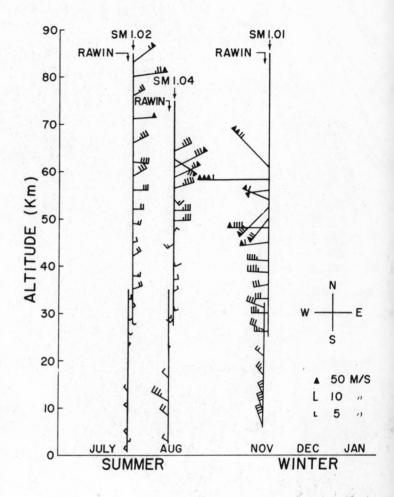

Winds in the air above Fort Churchill, Canada, in summer up to a height of 85 km (53 miles), and in winter up to 64 km (40 miles). Up to about 30 km or 20 miles the winds were measured by radar echoes from balloons (this is called the rawin method). Above about 28 km the results are based on grenade measurements. Where the two sets of measurements overlap they agree reasonably well. The wind direction is shown at each height by the line drawn from the vertical lines (see the compass cross). The wind speed is proportional to the length of the wind lines; it is shown also, to the nearest multiple of 5 meters/second, by the "flag" lines perpendicular to the wind lines (see the wind notation given below the compass cross). For example, at 47 km in November the wind speed was about 90 meters/second (or about 200 miles/hour). In this diagram the wind direction shown is that from which the winds come.

The greatest fully steerable radio telescope in the world, at Jodrell Bank, Cheshire, England. After ten years of planning it was completed in time to take a valuable and varied part in the IGY. The bowl is 250 ft. in diameter, has a maximum depth exceeding 60 ft., and weighs 750 tons. It can be rotated and tilted into any direction. It can be made to follow the motions of the stars by motors in the house shown at the foot of the picture. Above this house is the stabilizing wheel and, underneath, the hanging laboratory. This telescope penetrates farther into space than any other and can "hear" radio waves that began their journey millions of light years ago. It has played a specially valuable part in observing the earth satellites.

THE IONOSPHERE

In the upper atmosphere above about 40 miles there are many free electrons, separated from ordinary atoms and molecules either by ultraviolet radiation (by day), or in high latitudes by impact of solar and other particles that enter the atmosphere there with great speed. The atoms and molecules thus deprived of one of their electrons have a positive charge—they are called positive ions. Some electrons may attach themselves to an ordinary atom or molecule to form negative ions. The region where these charged particles are found is called the ionosphere. Its main layers are called E and F; the E layer is at height from about 60 to 80 miles; the F layer extends above it up to beyond 200 miles.

The ionosphere is studied chiefly by radio observatories on the ground, by what is called the vertical incidence method. Radio beams of changing frequency are directed vertically upwards in brief pulses. The radio waves are partly absorbed and scattered, and partly echoed back to the earth below—unless their

frequency is so high that they penetrate the ionosphere and are lost to outer space. By measurements of the echoes received from different levels, for waves of different frequencies, records are obtained that show the changing height of reflection for different frequencies, and also the frequencies above which the beam penetrates the E or the F layer. In this way it is possible to find the peak levels and the peak number of electrons per unit volume—the electron density—in the E and F layers. At the peak of the E layer, at about 70 miles, there are about 100,000 electrons per cubic centimeter at the equator; at the peak of the F layer, at about 180 miles, the number is about a million. The greater the abundance of electrons, the greater is the frequency required for penetration.

The main over-all aim of the International Geophysical Year ionospheric program was to determine the worldwide pattern of the electron distribution, in height and in geographical position, all over the earth—by day

The earth is affected in several ways by events on the sun that are often linked with sunspots. Here is a great sunspot group, photographed at the Mount Wilson Observatory, California, on May 16, 1951. The group contains many individual spots, each with its umbra (the dark part) surrounded by the penumbra (the lighter band around). Even the umbra is only relatively dark, in fact it is bright, though it is cooler and less luminous than the surrounding areas. As Galileo first saw with his primitive telescope, the spots move across the face of the sun, showing that the sun rotates. Strong magnetic fields exist in sunspots: the main spots at the two ends of such a group as here shown have opposite magnetic polarities. The extreme length of such a group may exceed 100,000 miles.

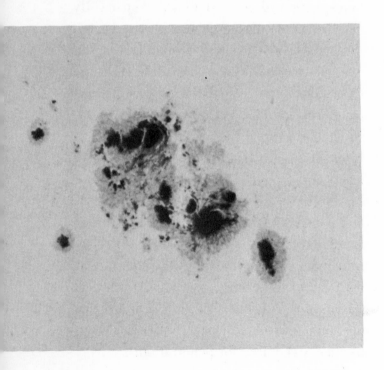

and night, at different seasons, and during quiet and disturbed periods. The disturbances are of two main kinds. Both are associated with unusual activity on the sun. At times there is a rapid brightening over some small area on the sun; this is called a solar flare. Simultaneously, if the flare is bright enough, radio transmission on certain frequencies is suddenly affected—the reception may cease completely during the period of the flare. This is because the atmosphere over the sunlit hemisphere becomes notably more ionized below the normal lower level of the ionosphere. This causes absorption of radio waves that usually travel upward through this region and have their path bent round the earth, so as to be received at a considerable distance away. Instead, the electrons in the lower newly ionized layer, which take up energy of back-and-forth oscillation from the radio wave, lose it by collision with surrounding particles. If the electrons are sufficiently numerous the radio beam can be completely absorbed. Radio signals of much longer wave length are at such times transmitted better than usual by having their paths curved round the earth at the underside of the newly ionized layer. Such an ionospheric disturbance is known as an SID—sudden ionospheric disturbance. The duration is usually reckoned in minutes up to an hour or two.

The other main kind of ionospheric disturbance is associated with auroras and magnetic storms. All three phenomena may begin a day or so after an outstanding solar flare; they are most intense in high latitudes, where alone the auroras are normally seen. Echoes from upward directed radio beams in auroral latitudes may suddenly cease, and transmission over long distances—and not only over the polar regions—may be disturbed for many hours or even for a few days. Such disturbances are called ionospheric storms.

The radio methods only measure the number of electrons. The nature of the ions can be found by rockets. The rockets that at Fort Churchill found the decrease of argon relative to nitrogen also identified the positive ions, by means of the same mass spectrometer.

In the E layer they found that the main positive ions are molecules of nitric oxide—a chemical compound of nitrogen and oxygen that is practically absent from the lower atmosphere. It involves the breaking up of nitrogen and oxygen molecules in the E layer, and the combination of oxygen and nitrogen atoms with each other. In the F layer the main ions are those of atomic oxygen.

It has long been known that above about 60 miles the oxygen of the atmosphere is largely broken up into its atoms. This process goes on to some extent even down to about 15 miles. But there an oxygen atom almost at once meets an oxygen molecule and combines with it to form a molecule of ozone $(O_2 + O = O_3)$. This gas has a long life there. Its presence there is important to human and animal life, because it is a remarkable absorber of ultraviolet radiations that would be hurtful to us were they not stopped by this layer of ozone, mostly above the tropopause. At higher levels, above 60 miles, the oxygen atoms have far less chance of forming ozone, and remain as atoms; above 80 miles they outnumber the oxygen molecules.

The nitrogen molecules are much less broken up by ultraviolet sunlight than are the oxygen molecules; but those that are broken up doubtless account for the formation of the

This diagram illustrates a rockoon launched by signal from its base ship (see p. 55). In flight the measurements made by the instruments within the rocket are signaled to the ship and there recorded. The rocket is shown as having passed through the lowest ionized layer of the atmosphere to reach the E layer, one of the main regions of the ionosphere. All the layers, including the one most highly ionized (the F layer), are affected by various emissions from the sun—visible, infrared, and ultraviolet sunlight, radio waves and X rays, and fast moving particles. These various emissions are enhanced during a solar flare—a sudden brief brightening of a small area on the sun's surface.

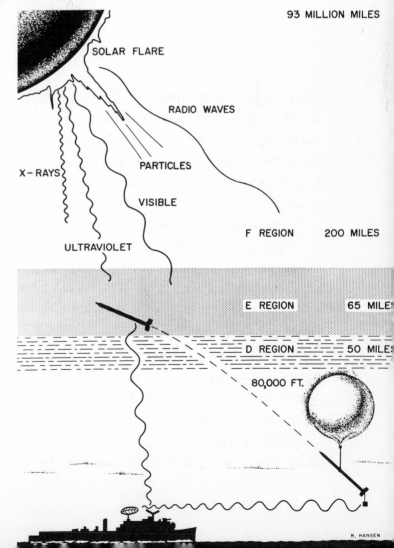

93 MILLION MILES

SOLAR FLARE

RADIO WAVES

X – RAYS

PARTICLES

VISIBLE

ULTRAVIOLET

F REGION   200 MILES

E REGION   65 MILES

D REGION   50 MILES

80,000 FT.

R. HANSEN

During World War II it was discovered that the sun sometimes emits radio waves of certain frequencies with immensely increased intensity. These solar radio storms are linked with other kinds of disturbance on the sun, including sunspots, solar flares, and bursts of X rays from the solar corona—the sun's hot outermost atmosphere. This picture shows the radio telescope of the University of Michigan. The bowl is 85 ft. in diameter. Among its tasks is to "cup an electronic ear toward the sun."

nitric oxide already mentioned. It is astonishing that these nitric oxide molecules are the main ones in the E layer. The theorists who study the photochemistry of the ionosphere have here an unexpected problem on their hands.

Rockets have also been used to make chemical experiments on the lower ionosphere, by ejecting into it nitric acid or sodium vapor or ethylene. The result has been extra ionization or luminosity of the cloud of injected gas—this may be a means of studying winds at high levels. The interpretation of such experiments is not easy, but they will certainly increase our understanding of the complicated chemistry of the ionosphere.

Winds in the ionosphere are studied by more than one kind of radio method. The vertically directed pulsed radio beams reveal that the ionospheric layers often change irregularly. By using three ground radio stations a mile or two apart it is sometimes possible to detect a similarity in the succession of the overhead ionospheric changes shown by their records. But the changes are not quite simultaneous at the three stations. The similarity can be explained by supposing that a space pattern of irregularity is drifting across the area. Comparison between the times of the changes at the three stations gives the speed and direction of the moving pattern—that is, the wind in the ionospheric layer concerned.

Another method uses the trails of ionized gas left behind by meteors during their swift passage through the atmosphere. The trail lasts only for a short time, generally not more than a few seconds. While it lasts, it can reflect back a signal from a radio beam directed perpendicular to it. If the trail is at rest the echoed signal has the same frequency as the radio beam. But generally the air is moving, carrying the meteor trail with it. Then the echoed signal is of higher or lower frequency, according as the air at the reflecting point is moving toward or away from the transmitter and receiver. By using a rotating radio beam, echoes are got from trails all round the station. This enables the speed and direction of the overhead air motion—which is taken to be effectively horizontal—to be found.

These methods of measuring ionospheric drifts or winds were applied extensively during the Year.

The upward directed radio beams also showed that at times there is slow but appreciable vertical motion of the ionosphere—so that the heights of the layers change.

Another IGY method of studying the changes of the ionosphere, especially at its lower levels, was by recording natural radio waves from celestial sources. Two prominent sources are situated in the constellations Cygnus and Cassiopeia. Of course the direction of these sources varies daily as the earth rotates. At times the received signals are weakened, indicating more than normal absorption in the ionosphere. This is particularly striking in high latitudes, where the ionosphere is often strongly ionized, especially in and below the E layer, by particles from the sun and by secondary X-radiation produced when the solar electrons make near collisions with the nuclei of atmosphere atoms. The X rays are more penetrating than the electrons themselves, and instruments on balloons have detected ionization by such X rays down to a level of only 20 miles above the ground.

Among the most remarkable phenomena of the ionosphere are the natural signals known as whistlers. Their frequencies are in the range of ordinary hearing—audio frequency. They start at a high pitch and descend to lower pitch. Sometimes they are repeated once or more. They are interpreted as signals caused by lightning discharges. They travel along a line of force of the earth's magnetic field, across the equator to the opposite hemisphere. The lightning discharge produces a radio noise that has components of many frequencies: those of higher frequencies travel slightly faster along the line of force than do those of lower frequency; hence the original sharp noise becomes a whine or whistler at the far end of its track. There it may be reflected back to the region of the lightning flash—where a whistler then follows the direct lightning radio noise at an interval corresponding to the time of transit to and back from the other hemisphere. Sometimes the passage to and fro is repeated once or more. When crossing the equator the whistlers follow the line of magnetic force to a great height above the earth. This indicates that even at some thousands of miles above the earth there are enough electrons—perhaps a thousand per cubic centimeter—to carry the signal. During the IGY an intensive study of whistlers was made in both hemispheres. Signals received at the earth's surface at two ends of the same line of magnetic force confirmed the above interpretation of the nature of whistlers. Observations of other low frequency natural signals, such as "hiss" and "dawn chorus," also provided much material for post-IGY study.

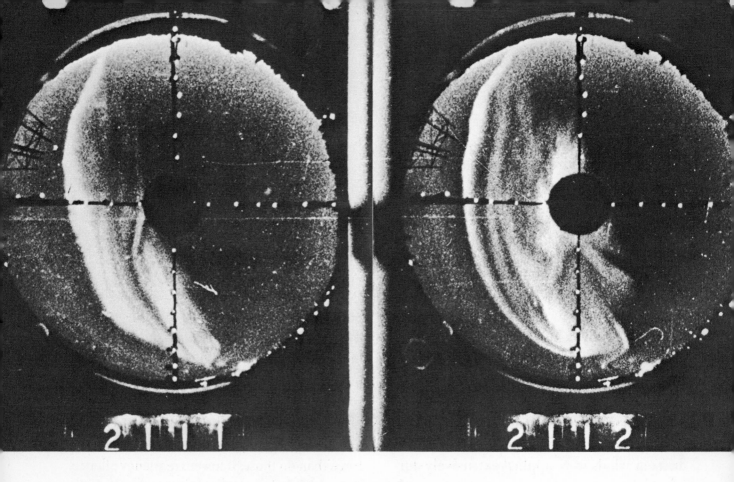

The Aurora or Northern Lights

The northern lights excite the wonder and interest of all who behold them. They are among the most remarkable and fascinating spectacles presented to us by the heavens at night. Their beauty can stand comparison with that of majestic or delicate cloud patterns by day or night, and with the marvelous panoply of sunrise or sunset skies. In color they may be generally less rich and varied than such dawn and twilight glows. But in compensation they often show more striking and rapid changes in form. In high latitudes their color is commonly a pale yellowish green (seen merely as a pale or whitish glow when relatively faint). But sometimes they are partly or wholly green, violet, or blue, or show more than one shade of vivid red.

In earlier times many fanciful interpretations were put upon them. They were some-times pictured as fiery horsemen contending in the sky. In parts of the north of England they were known as Lord Derwentwater's lights, because long ago a brilliant display coincided with—and was counted as an omen of—the execution (for armed rebellion) of a nobleman of that name.

The study of the northern lights was on the program of both the International Polar Years of 1882-83 and 1932-33, as well as on that of the IGY. But especially in high latitudes, where auroras are most often seen, they are often too widespread and quickly changing to be recorded adequately by any verbal description or hand drawing.

The auroral program of the IGY was far in advance of those of the two International Polar Years. In high latitudes, both Arctic and Antarctic, a network of about 120 sta-

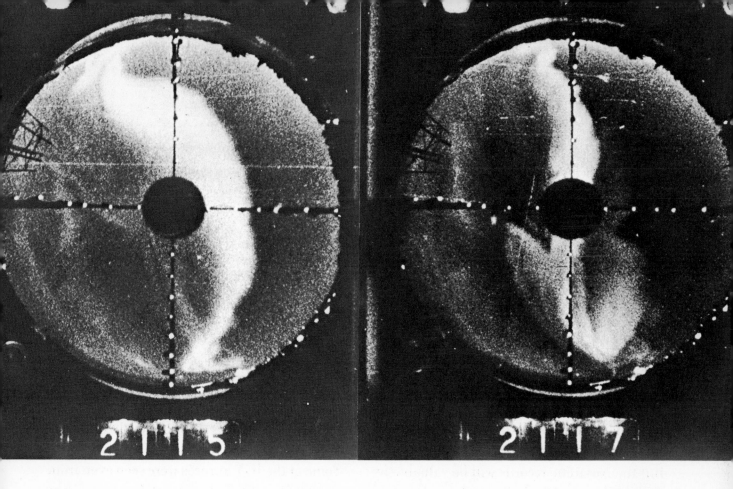

Below is shown an all-sky camera, at Fritz Peak, Colorado, of the type designed at the Geophysical Institute of the University of Alaska. Light from all over the sky, falling on a convex mirror, is reflected upward to a small circular plane mirror above. This again reflects it downward, through a hole in the convex mirror, to the camera in the box below. Thus, light from the whole sky (except the small part obscured by the plane mirror) is recorded on a film. This is moved on automatically each minute or every five minutes. The time is also photographed on the film. The mirror and camera are protected by a plastic dome. Four films thus taken (at the Geophysical Institute, Alaska) are shown above. On the original films the sky circle is 7 mm in diameter. North is to the right. Campus lighting shows at the edge of the circle. The time 2111 means 9:11 p.m. The films taken at 9:13, 9:14, and 9:16 are omitted. The pictures show how rapidly the aurora can change its form and location in the sky.

tions was organized, for the photographic record of the aurora. At these stations all-sky cameras were installed that automatically took a picture of the whole sky at every minute of the night (at some stations) or every five minutes (at others). These cameras produced an almost embarrassingly abundant photographic record of the aurora, that will take much time to study adequately. They will make it possible for the first time to get a fairly complete picture of the changing occurrence and extent of the auroral light over the Arctic night area; in the Antarctic the stations were necessarily much fewer, and the synoptic picture will be less complete. But the Antarctic records will be valuable by showing how nearly similar and simultaneous are the Arctic and Antarctic auroras.

At certain times, however, the aurora becomes visible from latitudes beyond its usual limits—for example, in the continental United States and the temperate regions of Europe. Outside the customary northern auroral regions—Alaska, Canada, Greenland, Iceland, Scandinavia, northern U.S.S.R.—all-sky cameras were much fewer. But there were several such cameras in the U.S., and one each in Scotland and Japan. Below 60° latitude, however, reliance for auroral observation had to be placed mainly, as heretofore, on eye observations. A great effort was made to recruit and organize and train visual observers to watch for and record the auroras that might come within their view. This was done not only in the U.S. and Europe, down to their southernmost limits, but in still lower latitudes—as in Mexico and South and Central America, in Australia and New Zealand, in Africa and Asia. The visual auroral watch-

ers were partly volunteers—seamen and airmen as well as landsmen—and partly professional—mainly meteorologists. The directors of many weather services valuably co-operated by instructing the observers at some of their stations to watch regularly for auroras at fixed night hours. Regional and national auroral reporters gave valuable aid in stimulating and co-ordinating this work in various parts of the globe.

Nature responded well to this increased attention. The opening night of the International Geophysical Year saw brilliant auroral displays, and others followed from time to time—notably on February 10–11, 1958. Some of the IGY auroras were seen even from the tropics. Such low latitude auroras are usually of a vivid red color, instead of yellowish green like most high-latitude auroras. On February 10–11, 1958, however, the aurora was brilliantly red, at times, even in high latitudes.

The aurora is in many respects still as mysterious as it is beautiful. By recording its form, color, and brightness from many places, it is possible to determine the true location of its luminosity in the atmosphere—its height and its geographical position in plan. Generally, it extends downward to about 60 miles, and it may extend upward to 100 miles on ordinary occasions. But it can attain far greater heights. This notably occurs when its luminosity is in a region of the upper atmosphere still lit by the sun's rays, though seen from places where the sun has set. In such cases its rays may extend upward to 500 miles or even more—showing how great is the height of our atmosphere in such sunlit air. The February 10–11 auroral rays were above

General view of the U. S. IGY Byrd Station, located at 80° S, 120° W, in Marie Byrd Land, Antarctica (see the map on p. 32). From the underground living quarters the aurora tower in the foreground is approached by an access shaft. Transparent plastic domes on the tower roof protect the all-sky camera and airglow photometers from the weather. These were placed in a tower to avoid trouble with drifting snow (see the Byrd Station views on pp. 51, 52). In front of the aurora tower is the garage roof. Behind, to the right, are shelters housing the deep drilling rig (for ice studies); the ionospheric sounding mast is on the left.

In the bitter cold of the Arctic night, an observer at the Auroral Observatory, Tromsö, Norway, directs a spectroscope toward an aurora. The light entering the three lenses is spread out into a spectrum, which is photographed in three parts, covering the whole available range of wave length. Ultrarapid film is used to permit exposures as short as possible, because of the rapid changes of the aurora in color as well as in form and sky location.

average in height and length; at times their lower ends were at the unusually great heights of about 150 miles.

The analysis of the auroral light by the spectroscope gives valuable information as to the nature of the aurora. The light comes mainly from the most abundant particles of the upper atmosphere—oxygen atoms and nitrogen molecules, neutral (whole) or ionized. But other particles also contribute—oxygen molecules and nitrogen atoms, neutral or ionized, and sodium atoms. Some of the light comes also from hydrogen atoms, and the wave lengths of their light indicate that these particles are rushing downward through the atmosphere with great speed—hundreds of miles per second. A narrow beam

of such particles entering our atmosphere will leave behind it a trail of atoms and molecules that are either "excited" or broken up (into an ion and an electron). The "excited" particles are disturbed in such a way that on returning to their normal state they may emit light of characteristic color or wave length. The color depends on the kind of atom or molecule that is excited and on the degree or nature of the disturbance produced by the adjacent passage of the rapidly descending particles. The light is that of the aurora; the ionization is not perceptible by our senses, but can be detected by radio methods.

It shows itself by the notable absorption, often complete, of the vertical pulsed radio beams ordinarily used to explore the ionosphere in high latitudes (as elsewhere). The radio beams from cosmic sources, though their frequency and intensity may be great enough to penetrate the ionosphere even at such times, also show notable absorption.

Another way in which the auroral ionization can be detected is by reflection of radio beams sent out at low elevations from stations many hundreds of miles away. Such beams may be reflected back by the ionized nearly vertical trails left behind by the rapidly descending particles that enter the atmosphere from outside during auroras. The reflection may be likened to that from meteor trails, mentioned on pp. 66, 67. By radar this enables the presence and location of auroras to be determined from afar, from points whence the visible aurora may be hidden by clouds. The radar method has a special value because it can detect auroras that occur by day, when daylight prevents their being seen.

By these various means the auroral observations will enable the daily and seasonal and irregular variations of auroral frequency and intensity to be more closely studied than ever before. Auroral maps will be drawn, similar to weather maps, indicating the location, height, forms, and motions of the auroras seen throughout the year. The spectral observations, and those of related solar, magnetic, and ionospheric phenomena, will be studied in connection with these auroral maps. In this way our auroral knowledge will be advanced, and some of the many puzzling auroral problems will be solved.

The particles that enter our atmosphere with great speed and produce auroras are certainly electrically charged—doubtless they are mostly protons and electrons, the two parts that together make up a hydrogen atom.

The close association between auroras and solar activity makes it likely that this ionized hydrogen gas comes from the sun—itself mainly hydrogen. Only if the particles are charged can it be understood why the solar gas enters our atmosphere mainly in high latitudes, and why its particles travel downward along the earth's lines of magnetic force—there nearly vertical. The earth's magnetic field will deflect such a gas, coming earthwards from the sun, so that its particles are guided toward high magnetic latitudes. The hydrogen lines observed in the auroral spectrum come from complete but excited hydrogen atoms formed when a solar proton is able, during its downward passage, to pick up an electron from the atmosphere. The electron may later be knocked off, and the proton may again form a hydrogen atom by a new pickup. Near the end of their paths the solar particles become scattered as they lose speed by many collisions.

The interval of a day or so between a great solar flare and SID, and the outbreak of a great auroral, magnetic, and ionospheric storm, is interpreted as being mainly the time of travel of the solar gas to the earth, from its source near the flare. But the intervening events that befall it near the earth are still mysterious. Not till they are better understood shall we know why the auroral light takes its many remarkable forms—varying from quiet uniform or rayed arcs to wavy bands or quickly moving curtains of light or diffuse pulsating patterns. We want to know also why the aurora sometimes comes beyond its usual limits to lower latitudes, and why its colors vary. Our understanding of such mysteries will be aided by the study also of solar and magnetic and ionospheric storms.

The Airglow

Chemical and electric changes continually go on in the upper regions of our atmosphere. They are caused mainly by sunlight (during the day) and by solar gas impinging on the higher latitudes (by day and night). These break up the atoms and molecules of the air into smaller neutral or charged particles. While these causes operate, and after they have ended, restorative processes go on. The sundered particles reunite with each other or enter into new chemical or electrical combinations. Some of these reactions involve the emission of light, of characteristic wave lengths. The auroral light is the most striking example. There is also a gentler and less variable light, called the airglow, that is emitted all over the earth at all times, by day and by night. By day it is invisible from the ground, owing to the brightness of the sky. But it can be detected from rockets that soar above the lower region of scattered sunlight. By night the airglow forms a faint luminous back-

ground, scarcely noticeable by eye, against which the stars are seen. The luminous layers of the atmosphere, that produce the airglow, are more than 30 miles above the ground, far beyond the clouds.

The IGY program included the study of the airglow at numerous places on the earth, distributed in latitude from Spitzbergen, and Thule in Greenland, down to the Antarctic. This is because of the information to be gained by observation and study of this light, about the chemical composition and processes of the upper atmosphere. The main particles that contribute to the light are neutral oxygen and sodium atoms, and molecules of an unstable substance called hydroxyl. These molecules (OH) consist of one atom of oxygen joined with one atom of hydrogen; they are formed when ultraviolet sunlight breaks off one hydrogen atom from a molecule of water (H_2O). The hydroxyl molecules radiate with special intensity in the infrared. If

The airglow is faint compared with the aurora, and consequently more difficult to observe. No attempt is made to photograph its form, though it is not uniform over the sky; sometimes it has brighter patches visible to the eye, though only rarely. Its spectrum includes narrow lines, particularly yellow—green and red (both from atomic oxygen) and yellow (from sodium). By filters the light of these pure colors is isolated from the sky background light, and its intensity measured by sensitive photometers. One such elaborate photometric instrument (left) that automatically scans different parts of the sky in succession, is on Fritz Peak, Colorado (see also p. 69).

our eyes were sensitive to that spectral region, instead of to light in the range from violet to red, we should not be able to see the stars against the bright infrared airglow.

The sodium atoms radiate with special intensity at twilight, when they are directly excited to luminosity by the sunlight. The airglow during the night gains its energy from that of sunlight absorbed during the day. This energy is slowly released as the sundered particles reunite or undergo other chemical reactions. The source of the sodium atoms is not yet known. Sodium in its ordinary form—a soft solid—is highly reactive in combination with water. The sea contains an immense amount of sodium in the form of salt (sodium chloride, NaCl). When winds blow up sea spray, evaporation may leave small salt particles in the air. Some of these may be carried to high levels by turbulence. Sunlight can break up molecules of salt into atoms of sodium and chlorine. This may be a main or minor source of the sodium that contributes to the airglow. Other possible sources of sodium atoms are meteors, and the clouds and streams of solar gas that enter our atmosphere in high latitudes and cause auroras. From there the sodium atoms might be carried by winds all over the world.

The airglow observations are made by complicated refined instruments called spectrophotometers. They reveal that the airglow is often patchy, and variable in the course of the night and from night to night and region to region. The interpretation of the extensive IGY airglow records will increase our knowledge of chemical and other changes that go on in the ionosphere, though proper interpretation will not be easy or quickly reached.

The Earth's Magnetism

There is yet another important source of understanding about the nature and phenomena of the upper atmosphere and the space beyond. This is the study of the variations of the earth's magnetic field. The fact may at first seem surprising, because the earth's magnetism is a property of the massive earth. Its cause is not yet fully understood, but is believed to be a system of electrical currents flowing in the inner liquid core of the earth. Unless continuously maintained, such currents would die away, owing to electrical resistance. Their period of decay might be reckoned in many thousands of years, but is certainly very brief compared with the age of the earth (a few billion years). Hence the electrical currents are believed to be maintained by a process essentially similar to that of a self-exciting dynamo: the dynamo produces electric currents by motion of some of its parts through the magnetic field generated by these same currents.

The liquid core of the earth, according to this view, must be in motion in such a way as to produce electric currents by flow of electrically conducting matter across their own magnetic field. In the core the form of the magnetic lines of force is believed to differ much from that of the lines of force we know, above the earth's surface. These lie nearly in meridian planes through the earth's magnetic axis (which is inclined by about 11° to the geographical axis, the north end being in the northwest corner of Greenland). In the core the lines have a pronounced component round the magnetic axis.

The magnetic field thus produced in the earth's core is the main part of the field observed at the earth's surface. This field is nearly the same as that of a small but very strong ("dipole") magnet at the earth's center, lying along the magnetic axis. It agrees still more nearly with the field of such a magnet located slightly off center—namely

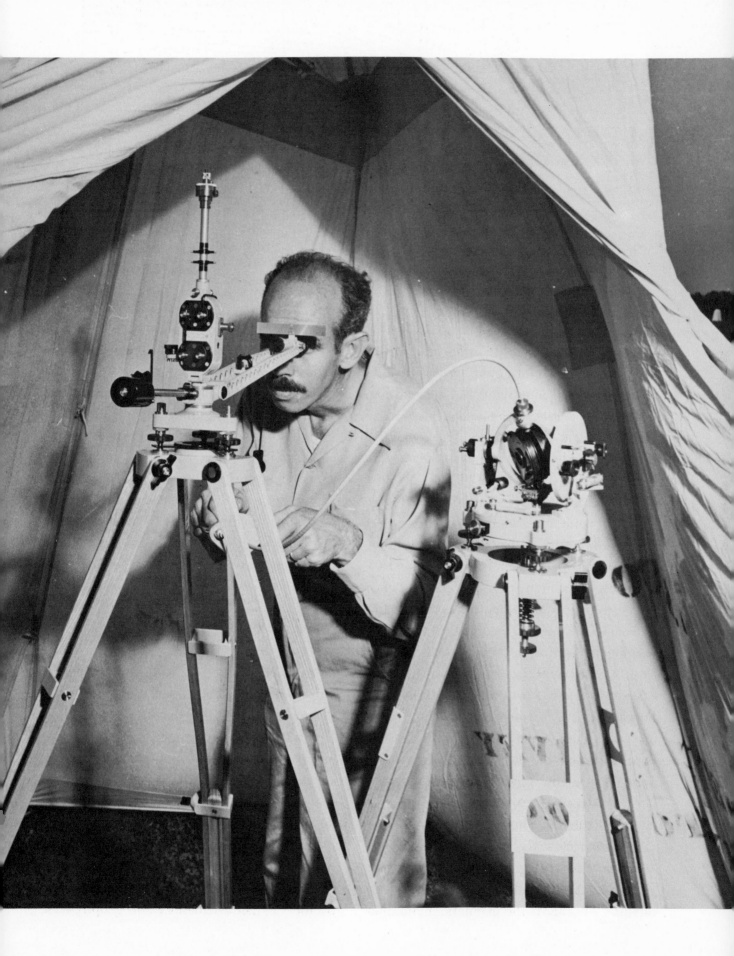

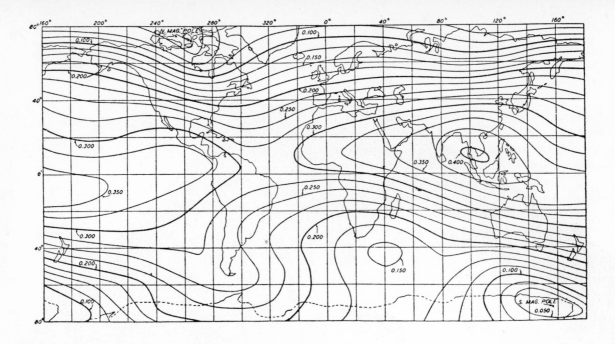

(at present) at a distance of about 250 miles from the center, along the radius that meets the earth's surface at about 16° north latitude, 150° east longitude. But in addition there are moderate regional departures from this "eccentric dipole" field. These may be caused partly by irregularities in the electric current system in the core. There are also more local irregularities of the field arising from magnetic minerals in the earth's crust.

Our knowledge of the surface distribution of the earth's magnetic field is based on measurements of its intensity and direction at very many points widely distributed over the globe. This knowledge can be represented graphically by magnetic maps. These may show its intensity F and that of its northward, eastward, and (downward) vertical components X, Y, Z; or instead of X and Y they may show the intensity of its horizontal component H, and the direction of this component. This is the direction of the compass needle, whose deviation from geographical north is called the (magnetic) declination D (or, by mariners, the magnetic variation).

These various magnetic quantities F, X, Y, Z, H, and D are called the magnetic "elements." Another is the magnetic inclination

I (or dip)—the angle at which the north end of a magnetic needle freely balanced about its center would dip below the horizontal. (Compass needles are not so balanced—they are weighted so as to make them lie horizontal.) The dip is 90° at the magnetic poles (north and south), where the needle rests vertical; in the Southern Hemisphere it is negative, that is, the north end points upward. The line of no dip ($I = 0$), where the needle lies horizontal, is called the magnetic equator. It does not lie along the geographical equator, owing to the obliquity of the magnetic axis and the additional irregularities of the earth's field.

The earth's surface magnetic field is shown on magnetic maps by "isolines" (from *iso*, Greek for equal), or lines all along which the "element" concerned has a given value. Hence the maps are called isomagnetic. The one of most practical importance is that for D: the lines of equal D are called isogones, the map is called isogonic (from *gonos*, Greek for angle). This is the chart universally used by mariners. The first map of this kind, showing the lines of equal D over the north and south Atlantic Ocean, was published in 1701 by the English astronomer and geophysicist

Magnetic compass needles are balanced to swing in the horizontal, although at most places the earth's magnetism tends to pull down one end of the needle and to tilt the other end up. The compass direction is controlled by the horizontal part of the earth's magnetic force. Its strength is indicated on this map, for the epoch 1922, by isolines (opposite). The horizontal magnetic force is greatest in low latitudes, and decreases to zero at the N and S magnetic poles, here shown. There the compass needle entirely fails. An example of an isogonic map (the first ever drawn) is given on p. 81.

Halley: a year later he extended it to cover much of the rest of the earth.

Such magnetic maps, as Halley well knew, gradually become out of date, because the earth's magnetism slowly changes. This slow change is called its secular variation. For a particular place it can be represented by a set of time graphs for the various magnetic elements. For the earth as a whole, it is shown by sets of isomagnetic maps for different periods—at intervals of 10 or more years. Such maps can be accurately drawn only on the basis of repeated measurements of the surface magnetic field. These must be made at suitable intervals and at a sufficient number of points well distributed over the earth. The changes, unlike the motions of the planets and stars, can only be observed and not predicted. This involves a great task of continual remeasurement of the earth's magnetism. The field has, in fact, never been fully measured—in particular, the observations have been inadequate or wholly lacking over large areas, for example in little visited ocean regions or in the Antarctic, and other land areas difficult of access. The task is partly a national one, as regards the territory of each nation; as regards the oceans and the Ant-

arctic, it is an international one, but it has never been adequately organized. The oceanic parts of the world magnetic charts have depended on the efforts of only a few nations.

There is need for a new world magnetic survey to bring our knowledge of the earth's magnetism up to date. Such a survey was not included in the program for 1957-58, for two main reasons. One was the necessity to devote special attention during the IGY to the more rapid, transient, magnetic variations, at an improved network of observatories extended over the globe. To combine this work with active magnetic surveys would have too greatly taxed the resources of the magnetic workers available. The other reason was that the IGY was meant to coincide with an active solar period, when the earth's magnetism is more than usually disturbed. This proved to be the case. Magnetic surveys are better undertaken during quieter solar periods. Hence it was recommended to the nations that took part in the program to undertake a new world magnetic survey soon after 1960, when the solar activity will be less. This project was regarded as a deferred but integral part of this great study of the earth.

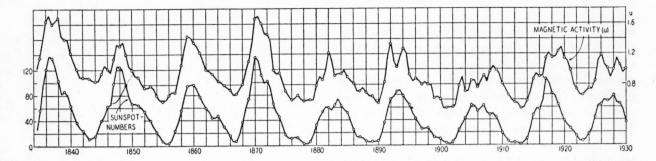

The upper curve shows the changes from year to year, over nearly a century (1835–1930), in the degree of disturbance or activity of the earth's magnetic field. The lower curve similarly shows the changes from year to year in the average number and area of spots on the sun, as indicated by the sunspot numbers (pp. 88, 104). Despite differences in detail, the curves are much alike, indicating in a striking way how greatly the earth's magnetic state depends on whether the sun is fevered or calm.

The Transient Magnetic Variations

During the IGY there were 190 magnetic observatories regularly recording the transient changes of the earth's magnetic field, each in its own locality. The records show that the field undergoes regular daily variations, nearly the same at different places in the same latitude, according to their local time. Occasionally disturbances modify the normal course. These interruptions are most intense in high latitudes near the auroral zone, where the polar lights can be seen on almost every clear dark night. In general the greater the magnetic disturbance, the finer and more extensive is the aurora.

Much is already known about the magnetic changes, both regular and disturbed. The regular daily change is caused by electrical currents flowing in horizontal circuits in the E layer, between about 60 and 80 miles above ground. The pattern of these currents is fairly constant as viewed from the sun, though it may irregularly change a little from day to day. It changes more regularly from season to season; the current circuit is stronger over the day than over the night hemisphere, and over the summer hemisphere than over the winter one. The current system as a whole is stronger at sunspot maximum than at sunspot minimum. It was this last fact that in 1882 led a Scottish physicist named Balfour Stewart to recognize that the daily magnetic variation is produced above the earth's surface—because in the massive earth there is no similar change in the course of the eleven-year sunspot cycle.

Balfour Stewart also then first suggested how the electric currents could be set up and maintained—namely, as in a dynamo, by motion of a conductor in the presence of a magnetic field. This is somewhat similar to the process in the earth's liquid core that maintains the main magnetic field; but the overhead electric currents depend on the main magnetic field, and only slightly modify the field at the earth's surface by their own additional changing magnetic field. The latter is recorded by the magnetic observatories, and from it the pattern and intensity of the overhead currents can be inferred. Their height, however, has to be determined in other ways. The radio measurements of the electron distribution in the ionosphere, with the aid of some rather complicated mathematical theory, indicate that the currents flow in the E layer. This can be checked by magnetometers shot through the E layer on rockets. The U.S. program provided for such a check. The rocket results appear to confirm expectations, though at present the check by rocket data so far published is not complete.

The 190 IGY magnetic observatories will provide abundant material for study of these "daily variation" electric currents, and may well lead to a better understanding of their day-to-day changes. These must be caused partly by variations in the airflow pattern in the E layer, and partly by changes in the solar radiation that ionizes this layer. Radio and solar data may enable us to separate the two causes. It may then be possible to check whether the changes in the airflow pattern are at all linked with dynamic changes in the lower atmosphere.

The moon exerts a tidal force on the earth. Its effects are most apparent in the sea tides, which are dominated by the moon. The sun exerts a minor influence on them. In the atmosphere also there are tides, but the sun's influence there much exceeds that of the moon. This is because the sun heats the air as well as exerting tidal forces on it. The lunar tide in the atmosphere is greater in the E layer of the ionosphere than in the lower air. By

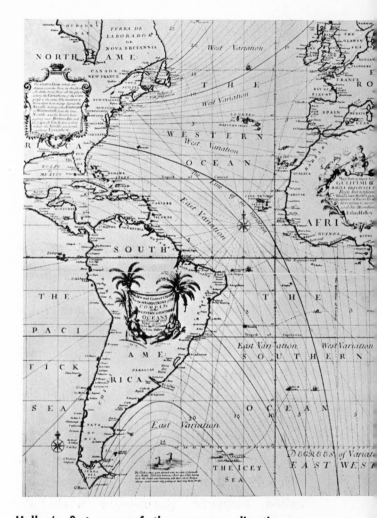

Halley's first map of the compass direction or "variation" over the Atlantic Ocean—and a little of the Pacific—(p. 78). Halley himself voyaged over the Atlantic in a small sailing ship, the "Paramour," along the course shown by the broken line, to get the compass measurements needed to make this map. At top left is his explanation of the map. On the right is a Latin dedication to King William III. The map of South America is notably misshapen because at that time ships could not well determine their longitude, having no reliable chronometers (p. 35).

For some kinds of study of the earth and the sun it is very advantageous to make observations at great heights. Hence there are several high altitude observatories in different parts of the globe. One of these, the Sphinx Observatory, is perched high in the Swiss Alps on a craggy peak called the Jungfraujoch (11,332 ft.). Astronomers and physicists come here from many parts of the world to use this excellent site and institution to study the sun, the cosmic rays, the airglow, glaciers, and high altitude weather. The observatory took an active part in several branches of the IGY program.

dynamo action it contributes to the electric currents in the ionosphere. Thereby it slightly influences the magnetic records taken at the ground. In most places, however, the effect is very small. Hence several years' observations are needed to determine it—by statistical methods. The increase in the number of magnetic records for the short period of the IGY is therefore unlikely to give much help toward a better understanding of this lunar daily variation of the earth's magnetic field.

The increase will, however, be valuable in furthering our knowledge of magnetic disturbances. Large magnetic disturbances—called magnetic storms—are worldwide. Usually they begin suddenly, and simultaneously all over the globe within about a minute. They are accompanied by intense and widespread auroras and ionospheric storms. Generally they follow a notable solar flare and its associated sudden ionospheric disturbance (SID). The SID marks a temporary increase of ionization in the region below the E layer, over the sunlit hemisphere. During this period additional electric currents flow there, similar to those normally present in the E layer. Evidently the same dynamo action of air flow is operating below the E layer, and is ready to impel electric currents there when increased ionization reduces the electrical resistance of the air. Attempts were made during the IGY to study *in situ* this increase of ionization and of electric current flow during strong solar flares, by shooting suitably equipped rockets.

The great magnetic storm follows such a flare after a period of fifteen hours or more. It is caused by a stream or cloud of solar gas shot out towards the earth, with a speed of the order 500 to 1000 miles a second—rapid, but far less so than the solar wave radiation that produces the sudden ionospheric disturbance (SID). Smaller magnetic storms may begin more gradually, and often cannot be clearly linked with particular disturbances on the sun. Both kinds of magnetic storms are caused by electric currents in the ionosphere, and also partly above or outside the ionosphere. The enhanced IGY magnetic records will enable us to find the pattern of these currents more definitely than before. A few rocket magnetic measurements were also made, in both high and low latitudes, during magnetic storms. These efforts were part of the many-sided attack on the associated problems of auroras and magnetic and ionospheric storms. At present there is great diversity of opinion among theoretical students of these problems. It is still uncertain whether the IGY will lead to a final solution of them, or whether this must wait until the ionosphere and the space beyond are more fully explored by rockets and earth satellites.

COSMIC RAYS, THE SUN, AND NUCLEAR RADIATION

The earth is continually bombarded from all sides by a rain of astonishingly energetic positive ions, mainly protons, but including also heavier nuclei. These have far greater energy than the particles of the clouds or streams of gas from the sun that commonly cause magnetic storms and auroras. Their speed cannot exceed that of light, but it is very close to this limit. The more nearly this limit is approached, the greater the mass and energy of a particle. That the particles called cosmic rays are electrically charged is shown by the influence of the earth's magnetic field on their distribution over the earth. This has been studied at ground level, and above the ground by instruments carried by balloons, rockets, or satellites. Among the instruments used are Geiger counters of several types, and also blocks of photographic film. The Geiger counters count the cosmic rays that pass through them, and the photographic film shows the results of their collisions with atomic nuclei outside or inside the film. Many new kinds of particles have been discovered in this latter way—generated by cosmic ray particles in some cases far more energetic than the fastest protons produced in present-day cyclotrons, synchrotrons, bevatrons, etc.

A great many cosmic ray particles are absorbed at heights of ten miles or more in the atmosphere. By collision with nuclei of atoms of the air they produce secondary particles—neutrons, mesons, and other stable or unstable particles, neutral or charged. These can be detected in the air or at the ground level; indeed, some cosmic ray primary particles are so energetic that they penetrate deeply within the ground, and can be registered by instruments placed in tunnels, mines, or in deep water.

During the IGY, records of cosmic ray products of more than one kind—specifically, of neutrons and mesons—were made at more than a hundred observatories distributed over the globe. In addition, various special cosmic ray measurements were made at the ground and in the air, using balloons, rockets, and satellites. The most startling discovery thus made (by Van Allen and his colleagues of the State University of Iowa) is that above 500 miles height there is a far-spreading region around the earth, inhabited by very energetic charged particles. This "radiation region" is a hazard to space travelers in this region. Its dangers are analogous to those suffered by unshielded workers on X rays or radium, or to those caused by nuclear fallout from atomic and hydrogen bombs. Fortunately the region seems not to extend right up to each pole. Hence safe exit and re-entry may be possible over each pole, obviating drastic measures (such as have been suggested by Singer of the University of Maryland) to sweep out the belts to reduce their intensity for a time.

The radiation region includes two belts, one extending between heights of about 1400 and 3400 miles above the equator, and the other between about 8000 and 12,000 miles. In higher latitudes the belts bend downward (see p. 85).

The particles in these radiation belts, where the atmosphere is extremely rare, are not ordinary cosmic rays. They are mainly less energetic charged particles trapped in the earth's magnetic field. They spiral round the lines of magnetic force, traveling back and forth from one hemisphere to the other. Finally they are scattered by collisions into lower levels of the atmosphere, where they lose their energy.

Their source is not yet known. One suggested explanation is that they are byproducts of cosmic rays. Some of the neutral secondary particles generated by collision of cosmic rays with atmospheric atoms will travel upward: as they have no electric charge their motion is unaffected by the earth's magnetic field. But they are unstable and after a short time they split up. This may produce charged particles, which are subject to the influence of the magnetic field. This process will certainly contribute, probably mainly to the inner radiation belt. But the major source, especially for the outer belt, may be charged particles from the sun, including some that are faster and more energetic than those that take about a day to travel from sun to earth (p. 82).

Earlier cosmic ray studies have been interpreted as indicating that the earth's magnetic field above the ionosphere differs in an unexpected way from what would be expected from our knowledge of the field at the ground. The worldwide IGY records of cosmic rays should throw further light on this question. But theoretical studies have been made during the year on the influence of the earth's field on cosmic rays, taking better account than heretofore of the large regional irregularities of the field. These studies suggest that the earlier expectations of the nature of the influence were imperfect, and that there may really be no discrepancy with cosmic ray data. Magnetic observations by rockets and satellites will in due course explore the outer parts of the magnetic field and definitely settle such questions.

It is thought that most of the cosmic rays that reach the earth come from far outside the solar system. But occasionally changes in the flow of cosmic rays on to the earth occur at

Below is a tentative picture, in section, of the Van Allen radiation belts. It is drawn on the basis of the exploration so far made; later studies will doubtless change it in some respects. The densest part of each belt is shown shaded; the other lines indicate lower levels of intensity. The numbers refer to the Geiger counts per second. The curve with arrows shows the nearer part of the outward and return flight of the Pioneer III moon probe rocket, launched on December 6, 1958, as part of the U. S. IGY program. The rocket traversed the heart of the inner belt once, and of the outer belt, twice, giving valuable confirmation of the presence of the belt and of the satisfactory performance of the instruments. The Pioneer IV rocket launched on February 17, 1959, showed that in the interval since December 6 the heart of the outer belt had been much extended outward—presumably by addition of new charged particles coming from the sun. The discovery of these belts is one of the major achievements of the IGY. As the belts are controlled by the earth's magnetic field, whose "geomagnetic" axis is inclined by 11° to the earth's axis of rotation, these vast appendages of the earth must undergo a large daily "wobble" with the daily motion of the geomagnetic axis.

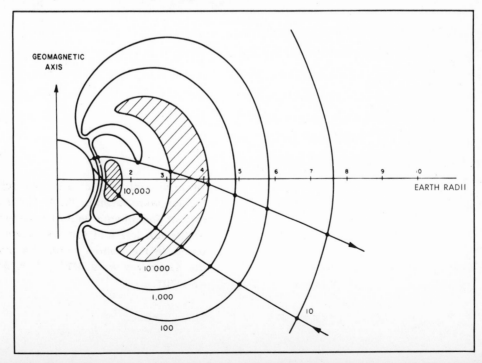

times of notable auroras and magnetic storms. These changes are sometimes increases and sometimes decreases. The increases are ascribed to extra cosmic rays being received from the sun. The decreases are ascribed to some blocking action due to the sun, that stops some of the normal flow of cosmic rays from reaching the earth. Usually these changes amount only to a few per cent of the whole.

But on February 23, 1956, there was a most astonishing brief increase in the cosmic rays entering our atmosphere, an increase of several hundred per cent. It was associated with a considerable solar flare, but flares of similar apparent nature, before and since, have not coincided with such a remarkable cosmic ray event. It can scarcely be doubted that in February 1956 the extra cosmic rays came from the sun, but their impact on the earth continued many hours after the flare ceased, and died away rather slowly. More than one fascinating theory has been proposed to account for the February 1956 event and its remarkable ionospheric conse-

quences, but the scientists who work in this field have not yet reached agreement on the explanation.

During the IGY some less startling but nevertheless unexpected events were revealed by cosmic ray recorders carried up to about 20 miles height by balloons launched in high latitudes. One of these events, in August 1957, produced much increased "counts," which on the basis of the detailed evidence were ascribed to X rays generated in the earth's atmosphere by collision of fast electrons from outside, with nuclei of atoms of the air. In August 1958 increased counts were observed, which were interpreted as due to very energetic protons able to penetrate down to that low level in the atmosphere. On neither occasion was there any notable aurora or magnetic disturbance—a fact that marks off these events from the more usual occasions of impact of solar gas upon the earth. It seems not unlikely that the cause was solar cosmic rays of less energy, in a beam of less intensity, than those experienced in February 1956.

These nine pictures of a stormy outburst at the edge of the sun were taken at the U. S. Air Force Solar Observatory at Sacramento Peak, New Mexico. The series starts at the top left and follows downward, in the two columns, to the bottom right. The time intervals between the exposures were 6ʰ27ᵐ, 12ᵐ, 5ᵐ, 11ᵐ, 7ᵐ, 12ᵐ, 7ᵐ, and 70ᵐ.

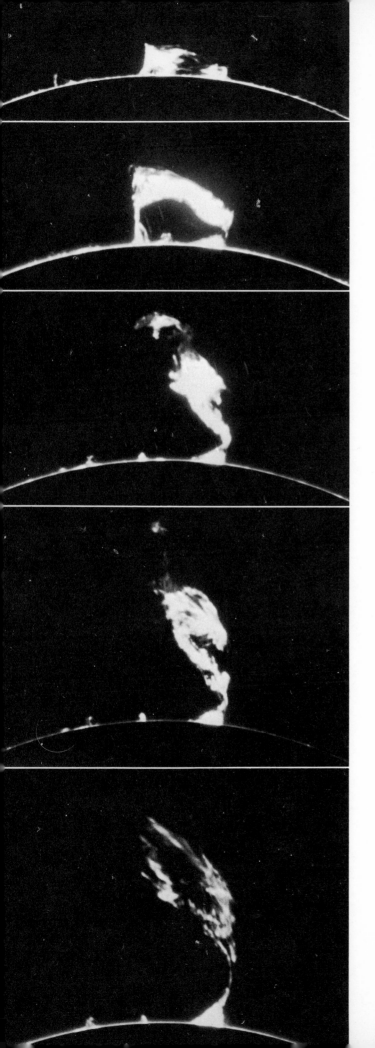

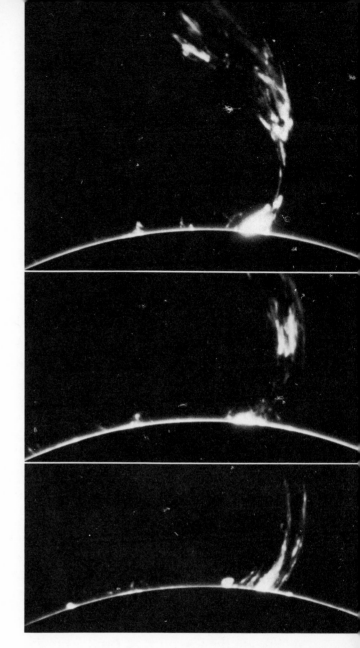

The Sun

The study of the sun in association with the study of many earth phenomena was an essential feature of the IGY. The solar astronomers joined the earth scientists in planning the program. New goals in solar observation were set, more ambitious than ever before. The aim was to keep the sun under observation which should be as nearly continuous and complete as possible, throughout the year. As the earth turns and carries some solar observatories into darkness (that is, as their day ends and night begins), it carries others into the sunlight, so that they can take up the watch on the sun. New solar observatories were organized, and the programs of pre-existing observatories were extended, so that the solar watch should be complete, with a margin of safety to cover cases where cloud prevented observation at some stations.

Solar astronomers have long recorded the sunspots, prominences, faculae, flares, and other visible kinds of changing activity on the sun's surface—but with gaps in the period of observation. Hence many interesting short term events were not fully seen, or were wholly missed. The solar corona, the sun's outermost atmosphere, was formerly observable only during total eclipses (p. 10). Through the invention of Lyot, a French astronomer now dead, the inner part of the solar corona is now observed daily at more than one observatory. The magnetism of the sun as a whole, and the far more intense magnetic fields of sunspots, were formerly observed regularly only at one observatory—Mount Wilson in California, where these magnetic fields were discovered by the great American astronomer Hale. During the IGY these fields have been studied by several observatories, with most interesting results. During World War II it was discovered that the sun at times emits great bursts of radio waves. Since then, in Britain, in Australia, in America, in Holland, the U.S.S.R., and elsewhere, radio observation of the sun has greatly developed. It was especially active during the year.

Thus a wealth of solar information of unprecedented range and completeness was accumulated. The IGY period coincided, as was hoped, with a sunspot maximum period. When the IGY was first planned, it was entirely uncertain whether, if the hope of its coincidence with sunspot maximum was fulfilled, the maximum would be weak or intense. The sun is a variable star, of a somewhat irregular kind. One sunspot cycle differs from another in duration, in the intensity of the maximum, and in the degree of inactivity at sunspot minimum. The best-known index of solar activity is the daily relative sunspot number R, based on the number and areas of the visible spots on the sun. Tables of R go back more than two centuries (p. 104). In the first six months of the IGY, and especially in October 1957, the values of R rose beyond all those previously recorded during this long interval. Nevertheless the activity was shown by an abundance of small and moderate spots, and few great sunspot groups appeared, such as made records during the previous sunspot cycle (maximum in 1947). However, several great magnetic storms and auroras occurred during the year, indicating specially intense impulsion of clouds and streams of gas from the sun.

The *Annals of the IGY* (p. 108) will include two volumes summarizing many of the measurements of the sun made during the year. This will be used intensively by many research workers in many lands, in correlating the events on the sun with those on the earth—leading to increased understanding of both bodies.

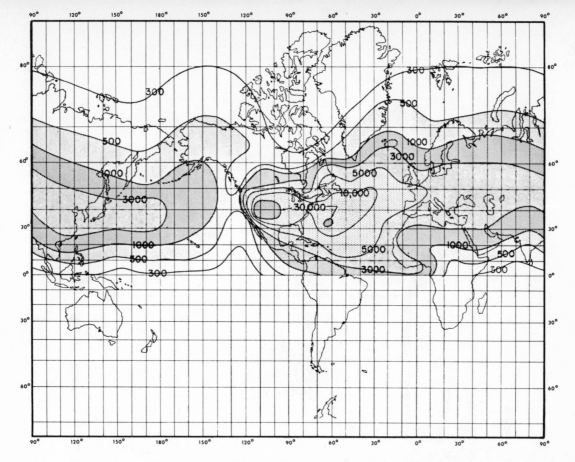

This map illustrates the intensity of "fallout" from low-level atomic bomb test explosions in Nevada, U.S.A., in 1953. The fallout consists of particles resulting from the explosion, that can be detected by their radioactivity. In these tests the explosion cloud did not enter the stratosphere, and the particles had much less far to fall, to reach the ground, than those generated in high-level atomic or nuclear tests. The Nevada fallout decreased rapidly; about half had fallen within 20 days. The fallout was measured using air filters in the lower atmosphere, or by collecting it on gummed films. As the prevailing winds generally blow from west to east, the fallout spread eastward round the earth, and less rapidly northwards and southwards. It was most intense just to the east of the explosion site.

Nuclear Radiation

In September 1956, less than a year before the International Geophysical Year began, a new item was adopted into the program. It was the measurement on a worldwide scale of the radioactivity of the air and oceans, of rain, snow and hail, and of solid particles deposited on the ground. Early in 1957 a simple scheme of collection and analysis was formulated and described. The principal aim was to use the radioactivity as a "tracer" for the better understanding of many weather and ocean phenomena. It included also the detection and study of artificially produced radioactivity—from bombs and from nuclear energy stations. These have already produced some worldwide pollution. Analysis of the radioactivity of ice and snow cores from the Arctic and Antarctic will help to indicate the level of natural radioactivity before such contamination began.

ORBIVM PLANETARVM DIMENSIONES, ET DISTANTIAS PER QVINQVE REGVLARIA CORPORA GEOMETRICA EXHIBENS.
ILLVSTRISS°. PRINCIPI, AC DÑO, DÑO FRIDERICO, DVCI WIRTENBERGICO, ET TECCIO, COMITI MONTIS BELGARVM, ETC. CONSECRATA.

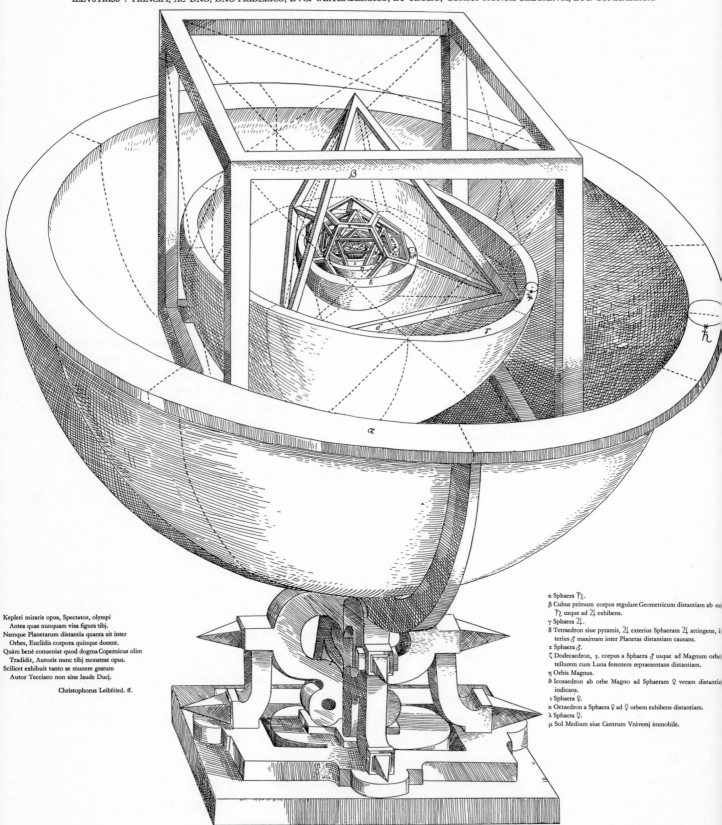

Kepleri miraris opus, Spectator, olympi
  Antea quae nunquam visa figura tibj.
Namque Planetarum distantia quanta sit inter
  Orbes, Euclidis corpora quinque docent.
Quàm benè conueniat quod dogma Copernicus olim
  Tradidit, Autoris nunc tibj monstrat opus.
Scilicet exhibuit tanto se munere gratum
  Autor Tecciaco non sine laude Ducj.

Christophorus Leibfried. ff.

α Sphaera ♄.
β Cubus primum corpus regulare Geometricum distantiam ab o
   ♄ usque ad ♃ exhibens.
γ Sphaera ♃.
δ Tetraedron siue pyramis, ♃ exterius Sphaeram ♃ attingens, i
   terius ♂ maximam inter Planetas distantiam causans.
ε Sphaera ♂.
ζ Dodecaedron, 3. corpus a Sphaera ♂ usque ad Magnum orbe
   tellurem cum Luna ferentem repraesentans distantiam.
η Orbis Magnus.
ϑ Icosaedron ab orbe Magno ad Sphaeram ♀ veram distantia
   indicans.
ι Sphaera ♀.
κ Octaedron a Sphaera ♀ ad ☿ orbem exhibens distantiam.
λ Sphaera ☿.
μ Sol Medium siue Centrum Vniversj immobile.

Excudebat Tubingae Georgius Gruppenbachius Ao. M. D. XCVII.

Science does not always progress with sure steps along a road seen clear ahead. Often trial steps in wrong directions are taken. When the error is perceived, new ways are tried. In time the right way is found. Then some steps along it may be easy. But again, the searcher halts in doubt. New right steps may follow only after a delay, sometimes long. They may be taken by other men, perhaps not in the lifetime of those whose progress they extend. Kepler took many wrong steps before he discovered his famous laws of planetary motion. Only after several decades were they explained by Newton. The picture opposite, taken from Kepler's book *Cosmic Mysteries and the New Star* (1597), portrays his (erroneous) idea that the distances of the planets are related to a nest of spheres and of the five regular solids discussed long before by Euclid—the cube, tetrahedron, and so on.

THE GROWTH
OF NATURAL SCIENCE

It is on the earth that mankind, in common with all other living things known to us, has evolved. Different races of men developed and spread over the earth, traveling on land and across the oceans. Century by century the face of the earth—its geography—was gradually explored. This descriptive knowledge, now nearly complete, is found in maps, atlases, and books.

Man is not content only to know such facts about the earth. He wishes also to understand what lies behind the facts—why they are as they are, and what governs their changes.

We live on an earth that in some parts seems to be a flat plane, though elsewhere mountains and valleys complicate its surface. The open sea seems flat. But long ago men of knowledge and insight realized that the earth is a globe.

The sun moves daily across our sky between its rising and setting, from our eastern to our western horizon. An ancient Greek astronomer asserted that the sun is a large distant body, whose apparent daily motion is due to the rotation of the earth itself—while this moves round the sun along a nearly circular path. These ideas were revived a millenium and a half later by the scientist-ecclesiastic Copernicus. Only after much opposition and dispute did they gain acceptance.

The astronomer Kepler, after immense pains of observation and calculation, concluded that the earth and its fellow planets travel round the sun in elliptic paths, with the sun at one focus of the ellipse. He found also that the line SP joining the sun to a planet P sweeps out the elliptic area at a uniform rate—so that the nearer the planet is to the sun, the more rapid is the angular motion of SP. He showed also in what degree the time of orbital revolution of the more distant planets exceeds that of the nearer planets—namely, that the square of the orbital time is proportional to the cube of the distance from the sun.

(An ellipse is a curve that can be described by a point P on a taut string of length l, with its ends fixed at two points S, S′; thus

SP + S′P = l. The points S, S′ are called foci of the ellipse. Different lengths of string will give different ellipses. The path of a planet P is an ellipse with the sun at one focus, e.g., at S. The line SP sweeps out area at a constant rate; for example, if the intervals of passage from P to P′ and from P′ to P″ are equal, then so also are the areas PSP′, P′SP″—bounded by the elliptic arcs and the lines joining S to P, P′ and P″).

These famous "laws" of planetary motion were found empirically by Kepler, that is, by trial and error, without guidance from theory or understanding of why these things should be so.

Newton thought deeply about the nature of the earth and the heavenly bodies. He conceived the idea that all matter attracts other matter. The attraction between bodies of ordinary size is too small to be perceived by our senses. But the earth is so big that its attraction is considerable. This in fact is the force that causes all bodies near the earth to tend to fall downward—downward being towards the earth's center. The same force, though weaker because of the greater distance, acts on the moon, and holds it in its monthly orbit round the earth. In turn, the earth and planets are pulled toward the sun and thus held in their orbits instead of traveling away into outer space. Newton was able to show that the weight of bodies near the earth, and the

The picture below, from *A View of the Heavens* by Richard Turner (London, 1783), shows the planets and their satellites as then known. It shows also three cometary orbits. Comets were thought to be supernatural omens until Halley, using Newton's laws, proved that they followed regular orbits and that their return could be predicted. The stars are shown much too near the outer planet Saturn.

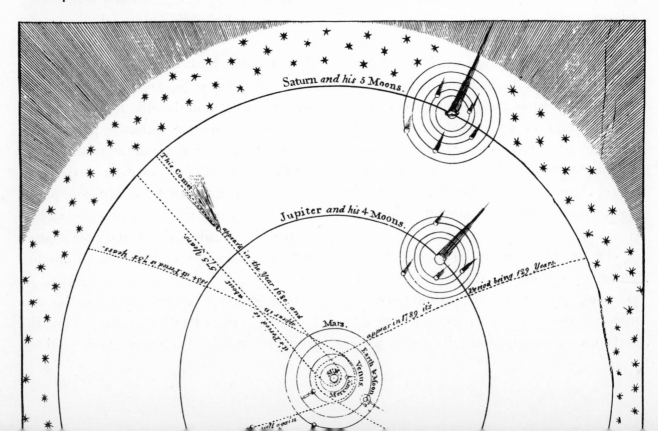

moon's motion round the earth, and Kepler's "laws" of motion of the planets round the sun, could all be explained by a very few simple assumptions. These are known as his three "laws" of mechanics, and his "law" of gravitation. The last states that two bodies attract each other with a force proportional to the product of their masses, and inversely proportional to the square of the distance between them.

These assumptions were found able to explain also a wealth of other facts, notably about many details of the motions in the solar system. These included the motions of comets, the slow change ("precession") of the direction of the earth's axis, its more rapid "wobbles," and the tides. His laws of mechanics gave an adequate basis for the development of engineering. Hence his assumptions came to be called Newton's laws of motion and gravitation. About two and a quarter centuries later, Einstein with deep insight extended Newton's law of gravitation. His modification of it (called the theory of general relativity) is unimportant in engineering mechanics. Its consequences are perceptible only in a few fine details of astronomy. Einstein, while thus correcting Newton's "law," had the utmost admiration for the greatness of Newton's mind. Newton, by these "laws" and his other works, profoundly influenced the development of science and technology throughout the centuries that followed. Einstein, by his relativity theory and other discoveries, opened new ways of thought and understanding of nature, thus changing human civilization and destinies.

The genius and discoveries of these two men of immortal fame represent outstanding peaks of achievement. Through them our understanding of nature took sudden great strides forward. Their ideas and example inspired and fertilized the efforts of immense numbers of other men whose thoughts likewise were turned towards the understanding of nature. Some of these efforts were devoted to the full and detailed understanding of the physics of the earth. This is a wide-spreading branch of science, appropriately called geophysics. It is but one of many branches of natural science, or the science of nature (as distinct from political or sociological or theological knowledge). Some of them may be called universal sciences, like physics, chemistry, mathematics. These study the nature of matter, and numerical relationships, independently of particular circumstances such as those on the earth, the moon, the sun or the stars. Other sciences—like astronomy, solar physics, geology, and biology—deal with more particular aspects of the universe. They require detailed observations, and they attempt by means of the universal sciences to explain what these observations reveal.

A science like physics can be studied wherever the necessary facilities and equipment are available. But a large body like the earth, varying much from one locality to another, must be studied in many regions. Co-operation and interchange of knowledge and ideas are of great importance for the progress of the universal sciences like physics and chemistry. In geophysics they are more than important—they are essential. Only by gathering together the knowledge of many aspects of the earth, gained by observations in many places, can the earth and its workings be understood.

The coat of arms of the Royal Society "for the improvement of natural knowledge," founded by King Charles II in London in 1662. The Society has powerfully aided the development of science through nearly three centuries. The motto "Nullius in Verba" signifies that the Society looks for truth about Nature not from metaphysical arguments but—as Francis Bacon urged—from observation and experiment and their interpretation. The Royal Society was the sponsoring body for the IGY program of the United Kingdom.

National and International Organizations for Science

In the seventeenth century national academies of science were set up. They brought together the comparatively few men in the nations concerned, whose enquiring minds were then devoted to the study of science. They did much to promote the progress and prestige of science in the leading countries. Visits and friendly correspondence linked these academies and their members in different countries.

More than a century ago the need to understand the magnetic changes of the earth led to the formation of an international Magnetic Union, guided by the great mathematician, astronomer, and physicist Gauss, of Göttingen in Germany. This led to the setting up of magnetic observatories in several parts of the world. At these observatories the changes of the earth's magnetic force—that controls the mariner's compass—were observed and recorded on a common plan. The organization lasted only for a few years, but the work continued, was improved, and was taken up in more and more countries.

Later in the century one country after another set up a weather service, to observe, record, and predict the weather. These services gradually grew, and their directors began to meet in conference together from time to time. They co-ordinated their experience, their instruments, their programs of observation, and their networks of observing stations. They organized means and codes for easy and rapid interchange of facts about the weather.

At first most of these weather services were in the countries of Europe and North America. Their domains surrounded the almost unknown Arctic region. It was natural to believe that this region might seriously influence weather changes in the surrounding countries. Hence it was judged important to study the weather over this region—despite difficulties of access and inhospitable conditions. For this reason the conference of directors of weather services (or meteorological directors) organized an enterprise called the International Polar Year (IPY). Eleven nations combined to send expeditions to different parts of the Arctic region, to observe the weather on a common plan, for a period of thirteen months—August 1882 to August 1883 inclusive. Two nations sent expeditions to high southern latitudes.

Besides weather observations the expeditions were given two other main tasks. The northern lights or aurora borealis had long excited the curiosity of natural scientists. It was known that they were more often visible in the Arctic than in temperate latitudes. Hence the expeditions were instructed to record them also. Moreover it had been learned, a century earlier, that auroras and disturbances of the earth's magnetism were often associated together. And already before 1882 the magnetic disturbances had been linked with new developments of civilization; they disturbed the working of the electric telegraphs—for example, those between Europe and America, and between England and India. Hence the Arctic expeditions set up temporary magnetic observatories. Their records revealed that magnetic disturbances are particularly intense and interesting in the Arctic—a valuable discovery.

International organization of science proceeded also in other directions during the nineteenth century. Earthquakes, though only locally destructive, set up waves that may travel all over the earth, and almost all through it; an international body to link seismologists—those who study earthquakes—was organized to exchange and discuss the records from the earthquake observatories that began to be set up in many parts of the world.

In mapping a city or a county no difficulty arises from the curvature of the globe. But in combining the maps of different countries and continents, to provide a world map, difficult questions of adjustment arise at the borders of the different surveys. To answer these questions it is necessary to know the size and form of the globe. This is not a true sphere, notably because its circumference around the equator exceeds that along meridians through the poles. Hence a need arose for discussion between those in charge of large-scale national surveys. This was met by the formation of an International Geodetic Association.

The astronomers likewise undertook international enterprises. Most of the active observatories were in the Northern Hemisphere, and part of the southern heavens was permanently beyond their view. When photography came to be applied to the stars, it was decided to map the whole heavens by this means. It was a great task that required the co-operation of many observatories, and the establishment of additional observatories in the Southern Hemisphere. This was achieved by international agreements between astronomers. They also formed an international group for the study of the complex changes and storms on the sun.

World War I (1914–1918) disrupted some of these international groups of scientists. When it ended a new beginning was made. The International Research Council (IRC) was established by the national scientific academies of the leading victorious nations. This Council sponsored several International Scientific Unions in the fields of some of the former international bodies, and also in new fields. Among these Unions was one for Astronomy,* one for Geodesy and Geophysics,† and one for Radio Science.‡ The IUGG included seven associations: for Geodesy, for Seismology, and for Meteorology, Terrestrial Magnetism and Electricity, Physical Oceanography, Volcanology, and Hydrology. In addition Unions** for Geog-

raphy, Pure and Applied Physics, Pure and Applied Chemistry, Biology, History of Science, and other sciences were formed.

The International Research Council was set up while the passions of World War I were still intense. The statutes drawn up excluded the scientists of the defeated nations. Efforts to end this exclusion soon began in the Council itself, and not only among the scientists of the neutral nations. Debates within the Council were at times heated. The exclusion evoked bitter feelings among some of the excluded scientists—whether they were nationalistic or internationally minded. When later the gates were opened to all, some of the excluded academies declined to enter.

The situation was relieved by transforming the International Research Council into a new body—the International Council of Scientific Unions (ICSU). The Unions themselves continued, but they removed any remaining exclusive statutes. These bodies all survived World War II. During that war their meetings were suspended, but the officers elected before the outbreak of war retained their functions. After the war ended the Council and its Unions recommenced their activity. There was no revival of exclusive statutes, and after an interval the formal Assemblies began again.

Between the two wars the directors of the weather services had maintained their conferences, despite the existence of the new International Association for Meteorology. Their association together became the International Meteorological Organization (IMO).

This organization took an important part in renewing the International Polar Year enterprise they had sponsored in 1882-83.

* International Astronomical Union (IAU).
† International Union for Geodesy and Geophysics (IUGG).
‡ International Union for Scientific Radio (URSI—the initials are in the order of the title in French, Union Radio Scientifique Internationale).
** Known by their initials, IUG, IUPAP, IUPAC, IUB, IUHS, etc.

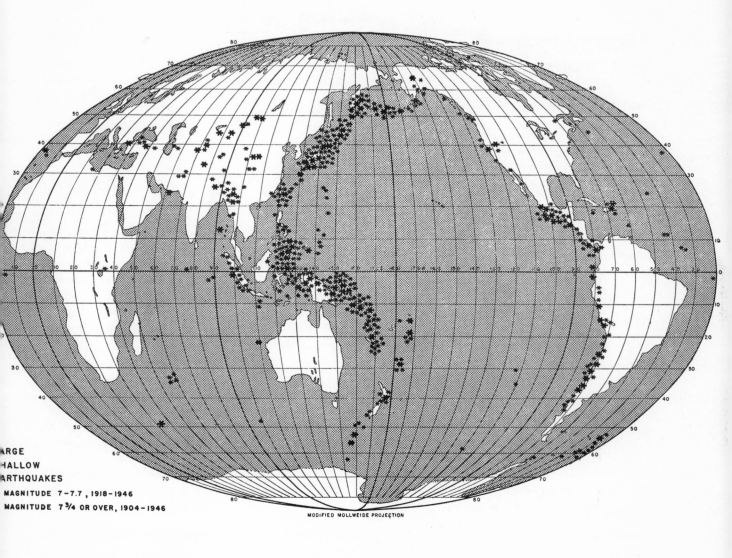

LARGE
SHALLOW
EARTHQUAKES

MAGNITUDE 7–7.7 , 1918–1946
MAGNITUDE 7 ¾ OR OVER, 1904–1946

MODIFIED MOLLWEIDE PROJECTION

This map shows where large earthquakes were generated at shallow depths (less than about 40 miles) in the earth's crust, during the period 1904 to 1946. The smaller stars correspond to earthquake intensities a little less than those of the earthquakes whose locations are shown by the large stars. The Bárcena Volcano, shown on page 13, arose in the area, much subject to earthquakes, south of the Gulf of California. The map shows that earthquakes are most frequent along continental borders and chains of islands (see pp. 23, 27).

Before the First International Polar Year many expeditions were sent out by various nations to study the arctic regions. Being uncoordinated with one another, some of their results were less useful than the corresponding ones gained in the First International Polar Year. In 1881 the U. S. sent out a polar expedition to Lady Franklin Bay, Grinnell Land, N.E. Canada. The expedition continued until 1884, thus taking part in the International Polar Year. (The U. S. main station for this Year was at Point Barrow on the arctic coast of Alaska.) A permanent station, here shown, was established at Fort Conger, the most suitable point north of the eighty-first parallel. It was near the coal seam discovered by an English expedition in 1875.

In the Second International Polar Year, 1932/3, the main British expedition went to Fort Rae, Canada, as its predecessor had done fifty years earlier, during the First International Polar Year, 1882/3. The 1932/3 expedition members, shown below, numbered six—five scientists and a mechanic (Kennedy, second from left). Four, including the leader, J. M. Stagg (sitting), were members of the British Meteorological Office. Later Dr. Stagg became its Deputy Director, and P. A. Sheppard (left) became Professor of Meteorology at the Imperial College, London. The other members were (left to right) W. R. Morgans, A. Stephenson, and W. A. Grinsted. The results of their observations and studies of weather, earth magnetism, and the aurora were later published by the Royal Society, London, in two large quarto volumes edited by Dr. Stagg.

The Second International Polar Year took place in 1932-33, for the same thirteen months as fifty years previously. It benefited from the co-operation of the Associations chiefly concerned—Meteorology, and Terrestrial Magnetism and Electricity—and of the International Union for Scientific Radio (URSI). The scope was mainly the same as before—weather, northern lights, and magnetism—but with an important addition, namely, observations of the Arctic ionosphere.

At the time of the first International Polar Year the ionosphere—the high "electrical" region of the atmosphere—was unknown. But during the year an article in the *Encyclopedia Britannica* was published, in which a gifted Scottish scientist, Balfour Stewart, first suggested that such a region must exist. More than 20 years later the suggestion was renewed, after Marconi first sent radio waves far round the bend of the earth. It was made independently by two Englishmen—Kennelly, a naturalized American, and Heaviside, an eccentric genius. Both of them saw that the waves must be kept from being lost in space, and be guided round the bend of the earth, by an upper electrical layer. This must act as an echoing curved wall does toward sound waves. A noted example of this is the "whispering gallery" in the dome of St. Paul's Cathedral, London—built by Sir Christopher Wren, contemporary and friend of Newton.

These ionospheric observations in the Arctic during the Second International Polar Year showed that the Arctic ionosphere is especially disturbed during auroras and magnetic storms.

After World War II, when the United Nations Organization (UNO) was set up, the International Meteorological Organization became attached to UNO under the title World Meteorological Organization (WMO) (p. 48). It grew until now about 100 meteorological services are linked with it. Another international organization for the advancement of education, science, and culture was set up under UNO, namely the United Nations Educational, Scientific and Cultural Organization (UNESCO). Like UNO itself, WMO and UNESCO are intergovernmental, and they are directly supported by subscriptions paid by national governments. They are special cells or organs in the body of world society. Their development may be likened to that of special glands and organs in the human body, as this has evolved from the lowliest least organized forms of life.

By contrast, the International Scientific Unions and their sponsoring body—the International Council of Scientific Unions—are nongovernmental. They are based on the national scientific academies. In many countries these are self-governing societies, and their members support the academies by their personal subscriptions. Many academies, moreover, have endowments provided by private benefactors. Most governments, however, make grants to their national academies to support services rendered to the nation, to aid their publications, and to contribute to their expenses in subscribing to international scientific bodies and in attending meetings.

Just before the beginning of the IGY a LIFE photographer took this photograph in the international IGY office at Brussels. The occasion was a meeting of the five-man Bureau of CSAGI, the special IGY international committee. Col. E. Herbays, left, was present to advise the Bureau; Treasurer of the International Council of Scientific Unions, he was a member of CSAGI, and its first convener. The others, from left to right, were V. V. Beloussov (member), L. V. Berkner (Vice-President), M. Nicolet (General Secretary), J. Coulomb (member), and S. Chapman (President).

THE INTERNATIONAL GEOPHYSICAL YEAR

In 1950 Dr. L. V. Berkner proposed that in 1957-58 there should be a third International Polar Year—25 years after the second. The suggestion was made in the then home of J. A. Van Allen at Silver Spring, Maryland, to him and his other guests. These were the American scientists J. W. Joyce, S. F. Singer, and E. H. Vestine, and myself, an Englishman. Berkner gave good reasons for a renewal of the International Polar Year after 25 years instead of the 50 that had elapsed between the first two Years. Technological advances during the 25 years had been remarkably rapid, and the Arctic had become a region of much greater interest to the nations surrounding it—for example, for radio communication and weather forecasting. The Cold War also added to this interest. Moreover the Second Polar Year had fallen at a time of sunspot minimum, whereas 1957-58 was expected to be at or near sunspot maximum, when many influences of storms on the sun affect the earth.

The proposal was welcomed by the group.

Later in 1950 Dr. Berkner and I joined in submitting it to the Joint Commission on the Ionosphere. This Commission was a link between the three Scientific Unions for radio science (URSI), geodesy and geophysics (IUGG), and astronomy (IAU). The proposal was endorsed by the Commission, which amplified the draft program and recommended the project to the International Council of Scientific Unions and the three Unions. The recommendation was adopted by ICSU, which in 1952 appointed a Special Committee to organize the project. In 1952 invitations were issued to join in a third Polar Year. The response to the invitations was modest. Many of the national academies were not greatly interested in sharing in polar scientific investigation. Later in 1952 suggestions were made in many quarters that the enterprise should be widened to include the scientific study of the whole earth. This was approved and new invitations were issued late in 1952. The revised invitation met a better response, and in 1953 the Special Committee (which became known as CSAGI*) decided that the International Geophysical "Year" should include the 18 months from July 1, 1957, to December 31, 1958.

Gradually more and more IGY committees joined the enterprise, finally to a total number of 67. Many of them sent proposals for the program. More of them sent scientists to the planning meetings, to help in settling the program and in considering matters of organization. Each IGY committee indicated what part it would take in executing the program.

The greatness and simplicity of the basic purpose of the International Geophysical Year—the common study of our planet by all nations for the benefit of all—made a strong appeal. Wide public interest in it was aroused by the press. The result was financial support on a scale more generous and adequate than any such international scientific enterprise had ever before gained.

The scientific scope of the enterprise also grew much beyond what was at first proposed. The original plans included the subjects studied in the two International Polar Years —weather, the aurora, the earth's magnetic changes, and the ionosphere—and, in addition, the cosmic rays. They are associated with each other and with changes on the surface of the sun. To understand them properly it is necessary to study them simultaneously—and also to study the sun. Hence the program included intensive observation of the sun in many different ways, and as nearly continuously as possible.

* The initials of the main words in the French title of the committee—Comité Spécial de l'Année Géophysique Internationale.

The officers of the Special Committee (CSAGI) were a president (S. Chapman), vice-president (L. V. Berkner), and general secretary (M. Nicolet); they formed the executive of the committee, until this was enlarged in 1956 by the addition of V. V. Beloussov and J. Coulomb. All members were appointed by international bodies. Fourteen scientists (called Reporters) had special duties, namely to co-ordinate and lead the development of separate parts of the enterprise. Two Reporters dealt with parts that affected more than one of the scientific branches. They were:

1) World Days and Communications: A. H. Shapley
11) Rockets and Satellites: L. V. Berkner

Twelve Reporters were concerned with the following scientific branches of the work:

2) Meteorology: J. Van Mieghem
3) Geomagnetism: V. Laursen
4) Aurora and Airglow: S. Chapman
5) Ionosphere: W. J. G. Beynon
6) Solar Activity: H. Spencer Jones, Y. Öhman, M. A. Ellison (in succession)
7) Cosmic Rays: J. A. Simpson
8) Longitudes and Latitudes: A. Danjon
9) Glaciology: J. M. Wordie
10) Oceanography: G. Laclavère
12) Seismology: V. V. Beloussov
13) Gravity Measurements: P. Lejay, P. Tardi (in succession)
14) Nuclear Radiation: M. Nicolet

During the planning assemblies each of the Reporters met with "working groups" of scientists. Each of these groups helped to

June 1957 (Advance Trial)

Sun.	Mon.	Tue.	Wed.	Thu.	Fri.	Sat.
						1
2	3	4	5	6	7	8
9	10	11	12	13	14	15
16	17	18	19	20	21	22
23	24	25	26	27	28	29
30						

July 1957

Sun.	Mon.	Tue.	Wed.	Thu.	Fri.	Sat.
	1	2	3	4	5	6
7	8	9	10	11	12	13
14	15	16	17	18	19	20
21	22	23	24	25	26	27
28	29	30	31			

August 1957

Sun.	Mon.	Tue.	Wed.	Thu.	Fri.	Sat.
				1	2	3
4	5	6	7	8	9	10
11	12	13	14	15	16	17
18	19	20	21	22	23	24
25	26	27	28	29	30	31

September 1957

Sun.	Mon.	Tue.	Wed.	Thu.	Fri.	Sat.
1	2	3	4	5	6	7
8	9	10	11	12	13	14
15	16	17	18	19	20	21
22	23	24	25	26	27	28
29	30					

October 1957

Sun.	Mon.	Tue.	Wed.	Thu.	Fri.	Sat.
		1	2	3	4	5
6	7	8	9	10	11	12
13	14	15	16	17	18	19
20	21	22	23	24	25	26
27	28	29	30	31		

November 1957

Sun.	Mon.	Tue.	Wed.	Thu.	Fri.	Sat.
					1	2
3	4	5	6	7	8	9
10	11	12	13	14	15	16
17	18	19	20	21	22	23
24	25	26	27	28	29	30

December 1957

Sun.	Mon.	Tue.	Wed.	Thu.	Fri.	Sat.
1	2	3	4	5	6	7
8	9	10	11	12	13	14
15	16	17	18	19	20	21
22	23	24	25	26	27	28
29	30	31				

January 1958

Sun.	Mon.	Tue.	Wed.	Thu.	Fri.	Sat.
			1	2	3	4
5	6	7	8	9	10	11
12	13	14	15	16	17	18
19	20	21	22	23	24	25
26	27	28	29	30	31	

February 1958

Sun.	Mon.	Tue.	Wed.	Thu.	Fri.	Sat.
						1
2	3	4	5	6	7	8
9	10	11	12	13	14	15
16	17	18	19	20	21	22
23	24	25	26	27	28	

March 1958

Sun.	Mon.	Tue.	Wed.	Thu.	Fri.	Sat.
						1
2	3	4	5	6	7	8
9	10	11	12	13	14	15
16	17	18	19	20	21	22
23	24	25	26	27	28	29
30	31					

April 1958

Sun.	Mon.	Tue.	Wed.	Thu.	Fri.	Sat.
		1	2	3	4	5
6	7	8	9	10	11	12
13	14	15	16	17	18	19
20	21	22	23	24	25	26
27	28	29	30			

May 1958

Sun.	Mon.	Tue.	Wed.	Thu.	Fri.	Sat.
				1	2	3
4	5	6	7	8	9	10
11	12	13	14	15	16	17
18	19	20	21	22	23	24
25	26	27	28	29	30	31

June 1958

Sun.	Mon.	Tue.	Wed.	Thu.	Fri.	Sat.
1	2	3	4	5	6	7
8	9	10	11	12	13	14
15	16	17	18	19	20	21
22	23	24	25	26	27	28
29	30					

July 1958

Sun.	Mon.	Tue.	Wed.	Thu.	Fri.	Sat.
		1	2	3	4	5
6	7	8	9	10	11	12
13	14	15	16	17	18	19
20	21	22	23	24	25	26
27	28	29	30	31		

August 1958

Sun.	Mon.	Tue.	Wed.	Thu.	Fri.	Sat.
					1	2
3	4	5	6	7	8	9
10	11	12	13	14	15	16
17	18	19	20	21	22	23
24/31	25	26	27	28	29	30

September 1958

Sun.	Mon.	Tue.	Wed.	Thu.	Fri.	Sat.
	1	2	3	4	5	6
7	8	9	10	11	12	13
14	15	16	17	18	19	20
21	22	23	24	25	26	27
28	29	30				

October 1958

Sun.	Mon.	Tue.	Wed.	Thu.	Fri.	Sat.
			1	2	3	4
5	6	7	8	9	10	11
12	13	14	15	16	17	18
19	20	21	22	23	24	25
26	27	28	29	30	31	

November 1958

Sun.	Mon.	Tue.	Wed.	Thu.	Fri.	Sat.
						1
2	3	4	5	6	7	8
9	10	11	12	13	14	15
16	17	18	19	20	21	22
23/30	24	25	26	27	28	29

December 1958

Sun.	Mon.	Tue.	Wed.	Thu.	Fri.	Sat.
	1	2	3	4	5	6
7	8	9	10	11	12	13
14	15	16	17	18	19	20
21	22	23	24	25	26	27
28	29	30	31			

January 1959

Sun.	Mon.	Tue.	Wed.	Thu.	Fri.	Sat.
					1	2	3
4	5	6	7	8	9	10
11	12	13	14	15	16	17
18	19	20	21	22	23	24
25	26	27	28	29	30	31

World Meteorological Interval [20 21 22 / 23 24 25 26 27 28 29]

Regular world day (11)
Regular world day at new moon (10)
Unusual meteoric activity 8 (but not world day)
Regular world day with unusual meteoric activity (17)
Day of total eclipse [12]

Adopted by CSAGI, September 1956

The IGY calendar, here shown, included an extra month at each end of the actual IGY. Many IGY procedures underwent trials during June 1957. Numerous IGY observations were increased or extended on the regular World Days—three or four per month—whose dates are circled. World Days of special character—new moon, total eclipse, or unusual meteor activity—are indicated. Special weather observations were made during World Meteorological Intervals—each of 10 consecutive days in each quarter year; their dates are enclosed in boxes.

develop the international program in its own field of work.

The IGY adopted an idea that went back to Gauss's Magnetic Union of the 1830's (p. 94)—that in many fields of work the number of observations should be increased during certain periods. In the earlier programs these periods were short—an hour or so, on certain days. For the IGY the above special calendar was drawn up. In choosing the special periods consideration was given to the phase of the moon, the occurrence of solar and lunar eclipses, and meteor showers. In addition to this calendar the plans provided for intensified observations of certain kinds on days that could not be certainly predicted in advance—days of special activity on the sun, likely to cause magnetic and ionospheric storms and auroras on the earth. This plan required the co-operation of the observers of the sun, who channeled their information to a prediction office near Washington, D.C. This office issued notices called Alerts, when the events on the sun seemed to foreshadow decided disturbances on the earth. During the Alerts the observers were expected to be ready to intensify their observations during a Special World Interval announced soon afterward, if solar developments were thought to warrant it. Elaborate arrangements were made for the rapid transmission of messages to the central office and to the various centers.

The International Geophysical Year stimulated observation of the sun so that it was kept under exceptionally detailed study. The information gathered will be studied later and will undoubtedly greatly increase our understanding of solar changes and their influence on the earth.

In the first International Polar Year the observations were confined to ground level. In the second one, fifty years later, they were extended to a height of about six miles. This was done by balloons carrying instruments and radio transmitters to signal the observations to ground recorders. At the time when the third polar year was proposed, the

Sunspots are the most evident and familiar sign of solar disturbance. The Swiss solar observatory at Zürich assigns to each day a number corresponding to the area and number of spots visible on that day. This diagram graphs the average sunspot number for each year, from 1755 to 1958. It well shows the changing cycle of solar activity, with an irregular period of about eleven years. The middle epoch of the IGY, namely the early part of 1958, coincided with a record sunspot maximum, for which the yearly average sunspot number was 194. The two previous records were decidedly smaller, 158 in 1778 and 152 in 1947. Since 1755 the *monthly* average sunspot number had exceeded 200 only three times— May 1778 (239), December 1836 (206), and May 1947 (201). In the present sunspot cycle this has already happened six times. In October 1957 the number reached the record value of 254 (see also pp. 80, 88).

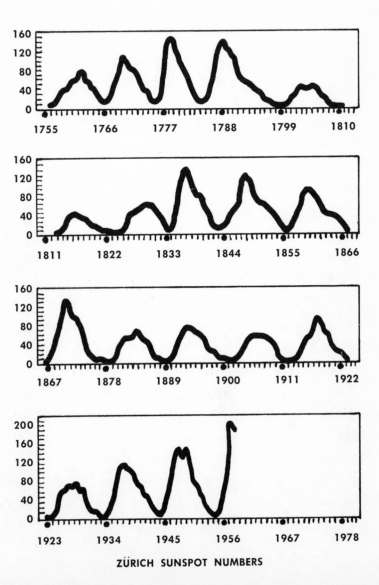

ZÜRICH SUNSPOT NUMBERS

exploration of the atmosphere had been ex- tended in the U.S. to far higher levels by means of rockets. At first rockets captured in Germany at the end of World War II were used; after these had all been fired, new rock- ets designed for this scientific exploration were made and used. Great skill and ingen- uity were shown in the design of instruments and methods to measure the properties of the atmosphere at high levels—a very difficult task, as the passage of the rocket through the air to be studied was extremely rapid.

High-level atmospheric exploration by small earth satellites was first marked as a possible item in the program in 1954. A year later, in 1955, the U.S. Committee an- nounced its intention to include such launch- ings in the program. In 1956 the U.S.S.R. committee did likewise. By that time the U.S. had begun to organize its share in the project, as regards design of the satellites, their launching mechanisms, their scientific equipment, and the organizations needed to observe their motion, to receive their signaled data, and to compute their future course.

In September and October 1957, a con- ference on the Rockets and Satellites pro- gram, in Washington, D.C. was attended not only by delegates from the committees that included rocket launching in their programs (U.S., U.S.S.R., U.K., France, Japan, Aus- tralia, and Canada), but also by others from the many countries that had decided to take part in the observation of the expected satel- lites and in the reception of their signals. The U.S. and U.S.S.R. IGY plans for satellite launching and instruments were described. Many other delegates indicated their plans and shared in the debates on how to make

The IGY World Warning Service (under the U. S. National Bureau of Standards) received information from solar, magnetic, ionospheric, and other ob- servatories in many lands. The solar data (sunspots, flares, etc.) were entered, as here shown, on a sphere representing the sun. With fair success the Service issued predictions about the occurrence of magnetic and ionospheric storms, and auroras, some days ahead. (See p. 104.)

the best scientific uses of the satellites. On the evening of October 4, before the final day of the conference, launching of the first U.S.S.R. IGY satellite was announced. Its unexpectedly large weight added to the profound impression made all over the world by this event. The radio signals, of lower frequency than had been expected, were strong and easily recorded. The difficulty of locating the object in the sky proved to be much less than had been feared.

A month later, on November 3, the launching of a far larger U.S.S.R. IGY satellite was announced. It carried besides various instruments a dog, "Laika," whose physical state was measured and transmitted by radio to the ground, until, after an appointed period, its life was brought to an end. A third U.S.S.R. IGY satellite was launched on May 15, 1958.

The plans for U.S. satellites first succeeded on January 31, 1958. Four U.S. IGY satellites were put in orbit. The launching dates of the other three were March 17, March 26, and July 26. The weights were 31, 3 1/4, 31, and 38 lbs.—the second was a test payload carrying only two radio transmitters. Between these U.S. successes were interspersed some launchings that failed for one reason or another.

Many of the scientific results of the U.S. and U.S.S.R. rockets and satellites are still provisional, but already it is clear that they make a very important addition to our knowledge of the space around the earth. The most striking result, first announced on May 1 from the two U.S. IGY satellites of January 31 and March 26, is the discovery of a region of intense particle radiation extending upward from a few hundred miles above the earth. These two satellites only indicated its

The U.S.S.R. success in the launching of their great IGY satellites was a source of justified satisfaction to the Russian people. At the All-Union Industrial Exhibition on the outskirts of Moscow, one of the pavilions is devoted to science, under the management of the U.S.S.R. Academy of Science. Models and diagrams of the satellites and their equipment are shown in one of the most visited rooms of this pavilion. They arouse great interest alike among Russian and foreign visitors.

existence. New instruments to measure its intensity and identify its nature were rapidly and successfully designed and installed in the fourth U.S. satellite. They revealed that the region contains energetic charged particles trapped in the earth's magnetic field (p. 85).

On October 11, 1958 a U.S. rocket was projected to a distance from the earth (about 73,000 miles) far beyond that attained by the satellites (which was up to about 1500 miles). It failed in its objective to reach and circle round the moon, but it provided most valuable information about the earth's magnetic field to a distance of nearly 20 earth radii. It also disclosed further information about the radiation region around the earth. A second U.S. rocket aimed to traverse the environs of the moon and to pass into orbit round the sun was launched on December 6, 1958. It did not attain the speed and distance intended, and like its predecessor it fell back to the earth, after rising to a height of about 63,000 miles above the earth. It revealed that the radiation region consists of two belts, one between 1400 and 3400 miles high above the equator, the other between 8000 and 12,000 miles. Though not a preannounced part of the U.S. IGY program, these remarkable flights made highly important contributions to the results (p. 85).

In stimulating the development of earth satellites and such "moon" rockets, the International Geophysical Year incidentally opened up a new era in the history of the human race. Like most outstanding advances in science and technology, it has great potentialities for good and ill.

An essential feature of the International Geophysical Year was the agreement between committees taking part in it that most of the observations—according to agreed lists—should be collected at World Data Centers. A full-time "Coordinator" was appointed to assist the central secretariat in the organization of this part of the enterprise. The U.S. and U.S.S.R. committees offered to set up and maintain complete international centers of this kind, whence any scientific organization or investigator could obtain copies of the material at not more than the cost of reproduction and transmission. Other participating committees offered to maintain such centers covering one or more parts of the program. The complete information at three or more centers will minimize risk of loss by fire or other catastrophe, and will be easily available to those who wish to study the observations, in whatever part of the world they may be. The information is available to all countries, whether or not they took part

in the enterprise. Scientists in countries that did not contribute to the observations may serve science by interpretation and analysis of the information.

The results of the two Polar Years were published nationally by the countries that took part in them. Only a few hundred copies of the reports were printed, and many important scientific libraries lack them. Some similar national reports may be issued for the International Geophysical Year in greater numbers of copies. But the central organization sponsored the publication of a new scientific journal of limited life—the *Annals of the International Geophysical Year*, or, briefly, the *IGY Annals*—to provide a widely available record of the enterprise. The first ten volumes contain the history of the planning and the programs and manuals and stations—including also a brief account of the two Polar Years. Later volumes will contain selected "central" observations, discussions, and reports on the results, catalogs of the information available at the World Centers, and bibliographies.

The planning and execution of the International Geophysical Year was marked by a most co-operative and harmonious spirit among the scientists of the 67 nations associated with it. Their common interest in its subject and purposes made it possible for them to work together despite differences of race, creed, or political organization. The enterprise was nongovernmental, sponsored by scientific academies, these being dependent for funds on national governments.

Questions of politics were almost excluded. There was only one major exception. This was the refusal of the Chinese People's Republic to adhere to the program if the par-

The oft-recurring passages of the IGY satellites around the globe were followed with intense interest in many lands. The satellites themselves indicated their presence by the radio signals they emitted. The smallest of the U. S. IGY satellites, whose signals are powered by solar batteries, is still announcing its invisible travels after more than a year. The giant radio telescope at Jodrell Bank (page 62) was able to measure the position of some of the larger satellites by radar. The U. S. IGY committee organized teams of "moon watchers" to observe the satellites visually. The great U.S.S.R. satellites at times were easily visible. Here three Swedish astronomers are observing one of them from the roof of their Astrophysical Observatory on the Italian Isle of Capri.

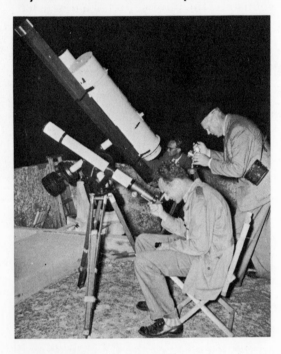

ticipation of Taiwan (Formosa) was also accepted. The co-operation of Taiwan was offered late in 1956 and accepted in 1957, two years after the Chinese People's Republic had adhered. The central IGY committee (CSAGI) felt unable in principle to refuse the co-operation of any scientific academy organized under a government in control of a particular territory. Such acceptance involved no political implications. It was with extreme regret that on the eve of the begin-

ning of the Year the central organization received word from the Academia Sinica, Peking, that its IGY committee had withdrawn from the program. Obviously the loss to the program was great. Participation in the program was not a matter for bargaining, but one of willing offering, by each academy according to its capacity and resources. Though the People's Republic may have proceeded, to its own benefit, with its intended program, up to August 1958 it had not contributed its information to an International Geophysical Year World Data Center. It may be hoped that in future it will yet do so, and that in any case the interpretation of the information stored in the Centers will be shared by Chinese scientists along with those of all other nations.

At the last meeting called by the IGY Special Committee at Moscow, the U.S.S.R. delegates proposed that the program be prolonged for a year, that is, throughout 1959. Delegates from some other committees were unable to endorse the proposal, as they had assured their national governments that the program would definitely end at the date initially set. However, all the scientists there gathered wished that geophysical and solar observation should be continued as fully as possible, at least through 1959. As a question specially concerning national organization, the proposal of the U.S.S.R. IGY committee was referred to the Advisory Council for the IGY, composed of the leading national delegates, one for each committee. This recommended that the IGY should be succeeded by an enterprise entitled International Geophysical Cooperation 1959 (IGC 1959), based on the continuance of the program for another year to the fullest extent financially

The first successful launch of a satellite by the U. S., an important part of the U. S. IGY program, sponsored by the National Academy of Sciences, took place on January 31, 1958, at 10:48 p.m., Eastern Standard Time. Being the first satellite of 1958, its astronomical name was 1958 alpha. The U. S. Army and the Jet Propulsion Laboratory of the California Institute of Technology accomplished the launching at Cape Canaveral, Florida. The satellite is the long slender object here shown at the top of the great Jupiter-C rocket.

possible for all the nations able and willing to engage in the new enterprise.

The International Council of Scientific Unions, meeting in Washington in October 1958, endorsed this proposal. It appointed a new Special Committee to handle the closing stages of the program after the central IGY committee ends in June 1959. The main task of the new committee is to promote the collection, publication, analysis, interpretation, and discussion of the International Year's observations. It will also give assistance to the 1959 continuation program. It should end its work at no distant date, and the Unions should then undertake the international supervision of the work of current co-operative research. At some time in the future a new intensified international scientific enterprise may be undertaken, perhaps far transcending the International Geophysical Year in range and power. At that time the remarkable success of the IGY will be an inspiration, and a guide, to the new effort.

The IGY nations which took part in the International Geophysical Year were as follows:

Argentina	Israel
Australia	Italy
Austria	Japan
Belgium	Korea (Democratic People's Republic)
Bolivia	Malaya
Brazil	Mexico
Bulgaria	Mongolia (People's Republic)
Burma	Morocco
Canada	Netherlands
Ceylon	New Zealand
Chile	Norway
Colombia	Pakistan
Cuba	Panama
Czechoslovakia	Peru
Denmark	Philippines
Dominican Republic	Poland
East Africa	Portugal
Ecuador	Rhodesia and Nyasaland
Egypt	Romania
Ethiopia	Spain
Finland	Sweden
Formosa (National Republic of China)	Switzerland
France	Thailand
German Democratic Republic	Tunisia
German Federal Republic	U.S.S.R.
Ghana	Union of South Africa
Greece	United Kingdom
Guatemala	U.S.A.
Hungary	Uruguay
Iceland	Venezuela
India	Vietnam (Democratic Republic)
Indonesia	Vietnam (Republic)
Iran	Yugoslavia
Ireland	

The International Geophysical Year Symbol, as adopted in 1955, and used in IGY literature and on IGY instruments in many parts of the world. The symbol shows the earth partly sunlit, partly in darkness, to indicate the influence of the sun on the earth; the Antarctic pole is shown, to stress the special attention given to the Antarctic during the IGY, as compared with what was done during the two previous Polar Years; and the earth is enclosed by the orbit of a satellite, to show this pioneer feature of the IGY enterprise—which in 1955 was a hope though not then a certainty. The symbol was used both unframed, as in the center above, and also framed in an octagonal border, with the names International Geophysical Year in two languages, as shown on the left (French and English) and on the right (Japanese and English).

PICTURE CREDITS

Page 10. Mount Wilson and Palomar Observatories
Page 13. Official U.S. Navy Photo
Page 15. United Press Photo
Page 16. Nat. Acad. Sci., IGY BULLETIN NO. 8, Feb. 1958
Page 17. United Press International Photo, U.S. Naval Observatory
Page 19. Nat. Acad. Sci.–IGY Photo
Page 20. Schweiz. Zent. für Verkehrsfördern, Zürich
Page 22. Nat. Acad. Sci.–IGY Photo
Page 24. Wide World Photo
Page 25. SCIENTIFIC AMERICAN, September 1955 (due to Prof. K. E. Bullen)
Page 27. Nat. Acad. Sci., IGY BULLETIN NO. 10, April 1958
Page 28. British Information Service
Page 29, top. British Information Service
Page 29, bottom. British Information Service
Page 30. Dr. D. W. Humphries
Page 31. Nat. Acad. Sci.–IGY Photo
Page 32. United Press Photo Map
Page 33, top. Nat. Acad. Sci.–IGY Photo
Page 33, bottom. United Press International Photo
Page 34. Leonard Bass
Page 35. Nat. Acad. Sci.–IGY Photo
Page 37, left. Sovfoto
Page 37, right. Wide World Photo
Page 38. Woods Hole Oceanographic Institution
Page 39. British National Institute of Oceanography
Page 40. Lamont Geological Observatory, Columbia University
Page 42. Dr. Harry Wexler, U.S. Weather Bureau
Page 44. Univ. of Michigan Photo
Page 45. Dr. Harry Wexler, U.S. Weather Bureau
Page 47. British Information Service
Pages 48 & 49. Sovfoto
Page 50. Official U.S. Navy Photo
Page 51. Nat. Acad. Sci.–IGY Photo
Page 52. Nat. Acad. Sci.–IGY Photo
Page 55. Official U.S. Navy Photo
Page 58. Univ. of Michigan Photo
Page 59. Univ. of Michigan Photo
Page 60. Nat. Acad. Sci., IGY ROCKET REPT. SER. NO. 1, 1958, paper by L. M. Jones, F. F. Fischbach, and J. W. Peterson
Page 61. Nat. Acad. Sci., IGY ROCKET REPT. SER. NO. 1, 1958, paper by W. G. Stroud, W. R. Bandeen, W. Nordberg, F. L. Bartman, J. Otterman, and P. Titus
Page 62. British Information Service
Page 64. Mount Wilson Observatory
Page 65. R. Hansen
Page 66. Univ. of Michigan Photo, Office of Naval Research
Pages 68 & 69, top. Geophysical Institute, Univ. of Alaska
Page 69, lower right. Nat. Acad. Sci.–IGY Photo
Page 71. U.S. Army–SIPRE, W. E. Marshall Photograph
Page 72. Wide World Photo
Page 74. National Bureau of Standards, Boulder, Colorado
Page 77. Nat. Acad. Sci.–IGY Photo
Page 78. S. Chapman and J. Bartels, GEOMAGNETISM, Clarendon Press, 1940
Page 80. S. Chapman and J. Bartels, GEOMAGNETISM, Clarendon Press, 1940
Page 81. S. Chapman and J. Bartels, GEOMAGNETISM, Clarendon Press, 1940
Page 83. Wide World Photo
Page 85. MISSILES AND ROCKETS
Page 87. Sacramento Peak Observatory, Geophysics Research Directorate, AFCRC
Page 89. HASL-42, USAEC 1958, paper by L. Machta, U.S. Weather Bureau
Page 94. C. R. Weld, A HISTORY OF THE ROYAL SOCIETY
Page 97. B. Gutenberg and C. F. Richter, SEISMICITY OF THE EARTH, © Princeton Univ. Press 1949
Page 98, top. INTERNATIONAL POLAR EXPEDITION REPT., Washington, 1888
Page 98, bottom. BRITISH POLAR YEAR EXPEDITION, Royal Society, 1937
Page 100. LIFE Magazine, © 1957 Time Inc.
Page 104. IGY BULLETIN, R. Hansen
Page 105. National Bureau of Standards
Page 107. British Interplanetary Society
Page 108. United Press Photo
Page 109. U.S. Army Photo